THE
STORY OF Y

a working cla

IAN DEWHIRST

MILLS & BOON LIMITED
London · Sydney · Toronto

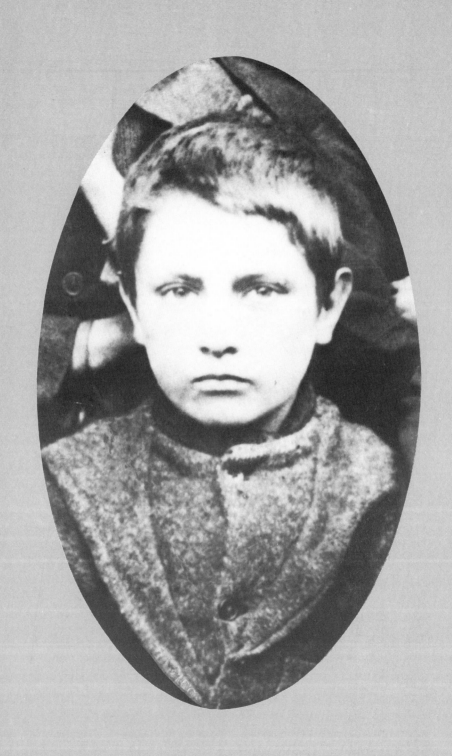

CHAPTER ONE

STANDARD 3

Standard 3 jostled out into the grey Board School yard where the photographer waited beside his tripod, sizing them up. From long experience, the photographer knew exactly how to resolve 40-odd excited boys into one compact rectangle. Divide them by five: front row of eight or nine sitting on the ground; second row sitting on forms; third row standing up straight; fourth row standing on forms; fifth row (the precarious ones) standing on forms on top of tables, leaning back for support against the railings. Leave a space for the teacher in the top left-hand corner.

Standard 3 were a mixed batch, and not every parent was going to buy a photograph—even the scarves, that some boys had instinctively put on, were ragged. Some of their faces were dirty (or were they bruised?), some of the young mouths already pinched and adult. There were several bad squint-eyes. The photographer, taking an experimental view under his black cloth, saw the toes of two boys on the front row poking out through their broken boots, was about to move them farther back but thought better of it—there wasn't time to shuffle the pattern about unduly, with other classes to follow.

'Fold your arms and look at me!' the photographer instructed, hunching back under the black cloth. Standard 3 froze, staring as one grimly into the camera. In the fourth row, above a casually knotted muffler, one mischievous tousled-haired face barely repressed a grin. In the third row, a clever, nervous lad wouldn't stop fidgetting. In front of him, in the second row, a better-dressed boy sat noticeably relaxed, hands loose in his lap, not even bothering to hold his breath. Miraculously, in that dismal yard under the grey threat of a wintry sky, the teacher had conjured up a white carnation for his button-hole.

So the photographer recorded the moment. Not all the class had folded their arms, after all. The grin of the mischievous boy with unruly hair had set into a grimace. The nervous boy had just raised a hand to his chin and his clenched, worried teeth. The placid face at his elbow gazed thoughtfully, confidently ahead.

*   *   *

The mischievous boy was Harry Riley. He lived in the middle of town, among the tall factory-chimneys in the crowded Ginnel, with no apparent father but an indeterminate number of older brothers and sisters. The Rileys were noteworthy chiefly on account of his big smart brother Stanley, a private in the local Volunteer Battalion of the Duke

1

of Wellington's West Riding Regiment, who turned the drab Ginnel suddenly heroic whenever he strode out on drill nights in his red tunic and dark-blue helmet surmounted by its silver spike.

The fidget was William Henry Berridge. An only child, he lived among the sprawling geometry of long streets ruled up the hills out of the smoky town. There were 20 houses to a row in Gladstone Street, each with a yard at the back and a square minuscule garden at the front. His father was thought to be doing quite well in the Co-operative Society's drapery department.

The home, in adjoining Peel Place, of Arthur Illingworth, the calm unruffled boy, was identical with those of Gladstone Street, except that it stood in a row of six and lacked a front garden. From its threshold, two steps (which his mother scrubbed daily, whitening their edges with her scouring-stone) led straight on to the hard-packed earth of the unmade street. He had an older sister Connie, and his father was a cabman.

These three, by virtue of their Sunday attendance (in the case of Harry, fairly casual) at the Congregational Mission, were friends. Arthur was a good scholar, William Henry outstanding, but only average Harry had, while in Standard 1, achieved the distinction of a personal mention in the headmaster's log-book: 'Harry Riley fell today in the playground causing a big lump to rise on his forehead.'

The Board School loomed like a citadel above the surrounding streets. There was an entrance at each end, uncompromisingly labelled, in carved stone, respectively 'BOYS' and 'GIRLS'. Its plain stone facade was alleviated by large windows letting in a generous light, and wrought-iron hot-water pipes kept it heated in winter. From a large central hall radiated classrooms crammed with forms and desks, their walls covered with pictures—in Standard 3 were assorted alphabets and multiplication tables; a map of Africa; a chart showing the difference between deciduous and coniferous trees; and prints of an elephant, a rhinoceros, Mary Queen of Scots about to be beheaded, Daniel in the Lions' Den, and a faithful dog resting its chin on a coffin.

All told, the Board School boasted 1,050 pupils, though most of the upper Standards were working half-time in mills, and the studies of the remainder suffered from truancies and recurring outbreaks of whooping cough and measles which, when reaching epidemic proportions, sometimes closed the school for weeks at a stretch and left many children with bronchial troubles. Otherwise, classes buzzed with a suppressed hum of reading, writing and arithmetic. Occasionally, in the main hall, or in the playground if the weather was

Above right Urchins of the Ginnel.

Below right The industrial heartland of Victorian Britain where emphatic chimney stacks take the place of church spires.

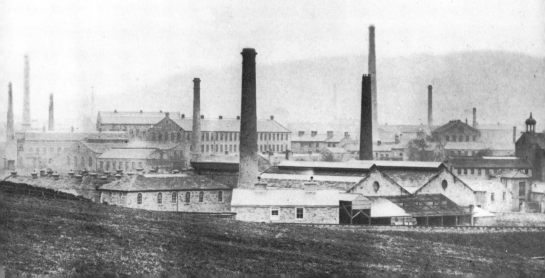

bright (this seemed very seldom, however), there were slightly more exuberant drilling and dumb-bell exercises. From time to time, as circumstances warranted, the headmaster lectured the assembled school on 'why copying is wrong' or 'honouring parents' or 'the evil attending being found in bad company'. The Bible provided a basis, not only for religious instruction, but for an extension of history and geography.

Very largely, Board School themes were also those of the Mission. Standing—less grandly—amid a squared framework of streets, the plain stone Mission likewise had classrooms leading off a main hall where worshippers sat in uncomplicated rows facing a platform with a reading-desk; the harmonium played to one side. 'In All Thy Ways Acknowledge Him,' advised a stencilled scroll high on the wall above the preacher, 'And He Shall Direct Thy Paths.' The only other decoration was a benign patriarchal portrait of wealthy Mr Brigg, who ranked very high indeed in the short history of the Mission: Mr Brigg it was who had lent £500 to the Building Fund for five years free of interest and, towards the close of that period, mindful of the difficulties under which its members laboured, had converted the sum into a gift. Otherwise, the bareness of the main walls was compensated in the Sunday School classrooms, where pictures abounded: missionary ships, native huts, again a map of Africa and Daniel in the Lions' Den.

At the age of seven, Arthur and Harry and William Henry and all their contemporaries had dutifully signed the Temperance Pledge. 'I do voluntarily promise,' their Superintendent had read solemnly over them, 'that I will not use Intoxicating Liquors as a beverage, nor traffic in them; that I will not give or offer them to others, and that I will discountenance their use throughout the community'; then each was presented with a certificate embellished with appropriate quotations—'If sinners entice thee, consent thou not' (Proverbs, i, 10) . . . 'Be thou faithful unto death' (Revelation, ii, 10)—which many, alas, were to lose sight of in later years!

The influence of the Mission extended far beyond Sunday worship; its Bibles and hymn-books were rivalled in importance by the heavy white crockery and enormous tea-urn in its well-appointed kitchen. The Mission had something to offer everybody. With its Christian Endeavour Society, its choir and Band of Hope and Young Men's Mutual Improvement Class, its rooms blazed with light and activity every night of the week. The hopes of a long-standing Extension and Organ Fund assured a busy round of At Homes, oratorios, bazaars, concerts, fruit banquets, ham teas. On Saturday nights (the Minister's reading-desk having been moved aside), the platform hosted a succession of tenors and sopranos, little orchestral bands sawing through their repertoires of valses, polkas, overtures and descriptive

Right The Mission.

4

fantasies ('Voyage on a Troopship', 'The Military Church Parade').
And, of course, recitations, always popular:

> 'Saint Peter stood wi' keys i' hand,
>   Says he, 'What do ye want, sir?
> If to goa in, yo understand,
> Unknown to me, yo can't, sir.
> Pray what's your name? Where are ye throo?
>   Just make your business clear.'
> Says he, 'They call me Parson Drew,
>   Aw've come throo Pudsey here'. . . .

Once a year, the Sunday School children would be given a treat and
taken on an outing. The Mission had been rather unlucky with its
outings. Several years ago they had put their scholars aboard a canal-
boat for a six-mile sail, but the horse towing the barge had fallen into
the canal and, although laboriously retrieved, was in no state to
continue. The following year, the children had been squashed into
carts, sitting on forms, but the tailboard of one had dropped, spilling a
row of girls into the road. In consequence Arthur's sister Connie
would always bear a scar near her left eye.

So now the Mission scholars relied on their own feet for outings,
and the day of their annual walk was Whit Monday, when other
denominations also paraded the streets and culminated (weather
permitting) in convenient fields for games and a tea; for not far
beyond the town, and before the high backcloth of moors, were
sloping fields glowing, at Whitsuntide, with a yellow sheen of
buttercups, their hedges hawthorn-white. Thither the Mission adults

would go beforehand, setting up trestle tables laden with buns and lemonade, scones and currant crackneys, and marking out distances for races. For most of the boys, though, the walking provided the main excitement. There was always a chance of meeting the Parish Church Sunday School—*they* marched behind a band and carried a banner—at whom, by obscure tradition, you shouted 'Church Bulldogs!', whilst they would inaccurately respond: 'Wesleyan Dish Clouts!'

A similar broad sense of community—or, at least, a general knowledge of who belonged to what—characterized Peel Place and Gladstone Street and most of the other houses spread row by row around the town (there was, by the by, a tendency to name streets after national heroes, according to the politics of the Town Council at the time of their building; either that, or after members of the builder's family, there were Cecil and Daisy and Ada Streets too). Arthur could, if asked, have given a precise enumeration of everybody in Peel Place, together with their occupations and condition. Three doors away, a teenage girl was slowly dying of consumption (her sister, two brothers and uncle had already died of it). Doctors were powerless, so some days she was taken to a maggot-breeding shed in a dismal moor-edge quarry, where she would sit with other hopeless consumptives purposefully breathing the gases from decomposing horses. Most of the patients' relatives pretended this was doing them good, but they kept dying nevertheless. The smell clung to her clothes, no matter how often they were washed.

In each Peel Place back-yard was an ash-place and an outside water-closet. The Town Councillors were justly proud of their new water-closets. (These did not, of course, apply in areas like the Ginnel, whose residents were still using the forthrightly-named excreta tubs, one tub to every five houses, emptied weekly during the hours of darkness by swathed night-soil men. Year after year, indeed, the Medical Officer of Health in his Annual Report would allude to the Ginnel and its neighbours: 'The walls are damp; floors often rotten; windows nailed up or broken; roofs defective; dust-bins absent or insufficient; no proper water-supply'; but no action had as yet been taken.) In Peel Place, too, every house had its own water-tap (in the Ginnel they all shared a stand-pipe out in the street), and comprised a living-room/kitchen, a 'front room', and three bedrooms—one fairly large and one tiny—plus a wash-cellar.

Arthur's mother was known as 'house-proud'. She filled her days with washing and mangling in the cellar, cooking and baking at the iron kitchen-range, waging constant energetic war against the soot-laden atmosphere, keeping the whole house spick and span and the front room frostily immaculate. The results showed in Arthur and his sister, who were always clean and nicely-dressed.

Right The Sunday School Whit Monday outing ended, weather permitting, with a 'nice' tea.

The house followed a precise pattern. The front room, used only on Sundays, remained for the rest of the week empty and cold. The living-room/kitchen, however, was by contrast warm and homely. Meals were eaten off a plain deal table, scrubbed white. Multi-coloured tab rugs relieved the stone floor. Last thing at night, the fire was banked up with coal slack, to be poked into new life first thing in the morning. Monday, being washing-day, saw the back street fluttering with clothes-lines when fine, the fire surrounded by steaming clothes-horses when wet. Wednesday was baking-day, sweet with warm scents of fresh bread and tea-cakes and scones. On Friday bath-night, the tin bath was carried up from the cellar—where it hung on a hook beside the mangle and peggy-tub—to become the centre of a cosy ritual in front of the fire. Sunday dinner, with meat, was the main meal of the week.

Arthur's father, the cabman, unlike most of the clerk and mill-worker occupants of Peel Place, tended to sleep late in a morning and stay out till all hours of the night, coming home muffled and mackintoshed but often cold and wet. There existed, however, a multitude of philanthropic organisations, one of which had recently espoused the interests of Arthur's father: the Hackney Carriage Committee had canvassed subscriptions and provided a pretty mock-Gothic cabmen's shelter, containing six seats, a stove and a wash-basin, and with windows of coloured glass.

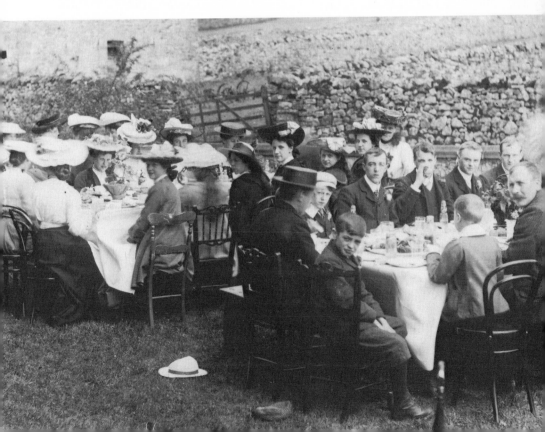

As for the town itself, this had first grown then over-grown during the past century, first on cotton, later on worsted. Also it clanged and fumed with foundries and engineering works. It was built almost wholly of grey stone quarried from its rainy neighbouring hills. Its Town Council was regarded as reasonably enterprising: it boasted two parks and a museum, a street of solid, ornamented banks, whilst its baths and wash-houses were a model for the county. It had many public-houses, and almost as many places of worship. Centred upon a broad valley, it lay, as viewed from any of its surrounding hills, under a perpetual grey fog, six days out of every seven.

*   *   *

The pleasures of Arthur and Harry and William Henry were, for the most part, simple and self-made. After school, the streets and alleys (despite the parks, which were impeccably kept and patrolled by zealous rangers) rang with children's voices, the stamp of hopscotch and the swish of skipping-ropes: 'Bluebells, cockle-shells, eevory-ivory-over' . . . 'Raspberry, strawberry, gooseberry jam; tell me the name of your young man' . . . 'Salt, pepper, vinegar, mustard' . . . 'Queenie, Queenie Caroline, dipped her hair in turpentine' . . . Boys played for hours at a time, ton-weights-coming-on, hitting piggy-sticks with old broom-handles, kicking tin-cans, flicking buttons—tin, brass, pearl, bone, of an endless variety—into holes and picking them out again with a wet thumb. Every once in a while appeared a swarthy foreigner with a big chained shaggy bear which lumbered up on to its hind legs and held out a mug in its great front paws, collecting coppers. The foreigner, knowing better than to come to the likes of Peel Place and Gladstone Street, performed outside finer and more generous houses; to which, nevertheless, the children flocked from far and wide to watch.

Two events especially enlivened the year. Christmas helped light the way briefly through grim winter; and each June—exactly spaced between one Christmas and the next—the Friendly Societies ('Benefits: £10 at death of member, £6 member's wife, £4 second or subsequent wife') held their Gala, when Mr Berridge, as a member of the Gala Committee, enjoyed a Saturday of importance, pacing brusquely in his Sunday best between watching crowds, marshalling the procession.

This was, in truth, an unearthly spectacle wherein you saw familiar people in strange guises, for the Friendly Societies paraded in full regalia, the Independent Order of Oddfellows wearing aprons and sashes, the Ancient Order of Foresters carrying bows and arrows, the Society of Operative Masons riding on waggons chipping ineffectually at blocks of stone. For an hour and more, slowly and with frequent

Right 'A huge and ever-growing dome': a balloon being inflated.

8

halts, their procession passed any given point in town, rhythmic with bands of brass and fife and concertina, made merry by fancy-dress comics and decorated bicycles hidden beneath flowers. Floats and carts (for many prizes were offered) swayed with unaccustomed smoothness behind big groomed horses tossing their plumed heads and jingling their polished brasses. Fire-engines, and the helmets of their crews, shone like mirrors.

For Gala Day, the normally sedate open spaces of Victoria Park were given up to a fair and entertainments. Jostling amidst unprecedented crowds—half-price trains ran in from Leeds and Bradford—Arthur and Harry and William Henry would wrestle for vantage-points from which to goggle at the Zamezou Troupe of Lightning Acrobats (straight from the Crystal Palace), at Professor Rennef, juggling King of the Cannon-Ball, at the Marvellous Dunlops, Little Dan (the smallest clown in the world) and Master Smith, the youngest Indian Club performer known. . . .

But the highlight usually came during the evening when, out of the thickest of the press, would slowly swell a huge and ever-growing dome. Some years this was silver, other times scarlet or orange, and once it had arisen fully-fledged bearing a colossal (90 feet high, to be precise) portrait of the Queen: a bright silken balloon, with a trapeze bar swinging beneath it on which, in shirt-sleeves and watch-chain, a

daring aeronaut would float waving up above a sea of gawping faces until he was no more than a speck in the high June sky. Then—if the evening was very clear, and if the breeze hadn't carried him too far away—you could just see him jump and his parachute open out. Usually, however, you scarcely saw this, sometimes not at all, but the aeronaut always made a triumphal return into the Park later in the evening (except one year, when he had broken both legs). Later, after dark, there would be a fireworks display with fizzing, popping set-pieces ('Grand Naval Battle', 'Long Live the Mayor', 'God Save Our Queen'); the united bands played the National Anthem, brass, fifes and concertinas all mixed in together, and everybody tramped happily homewards, or back to the half-price railway station.

Twice a year too, in May and November, came the horse and cattle fair, when between the stately banks the thoroughfares filled with sheep and cows and fine stud bulls, farmers and dealers, loungers and boys, everyone armed for the occasion with a stick or switch. Traditionally, the Board School always enjoyed a holiday, its yard being used for selling and trotting horses. Afterwards, the fire brigade would bring their hoses and swill the streets and school-yard clean.

Then there were other, more random entertainments, circuses occasionally setting up their marquees; and just once an extraordinary visit from Barnum and Bailey's Greatest Show on Earth. Weeks in advance, hoardings and house-sides sprouted the biggest, gaudiest posters: 'The Greatest Aerial Acts ever Devised. The Grandest Riding ever seen. The Cleverest Acrobats ever beheld. The Best Gymnasts ever Performing. The Most Thrilling Feats ever witnessed. The Greatest and Most Superb Show Ever Devised by Man. In Three Big Equestrian Rings, on Two Huge Platforms, an Immense Racing Track, and Spacious Aerial Enclave . . .'

For once, the dullest scholars professed an urge to read. Their teacher used Barnum and Bailey's advertising to good effect. Standard 3 did sums based on the Show's '70 railway cars, each one nearly 60 feet long, made up into 4 enormous trains of 17 cars each'; everybody was taught that 'ponderous pachyderms' were elephants; and their knowledge of the animal world was enriched, on a Saturday morning, by simply watching the street parade—cages of lions, tigers and leopards, panthers, hyenas, bears and wolves; a chariot drawn by zebras; lumbering lines of elephants and camels; and Johanna, 'the only gorilla in captivity'.

But what would stick in the memory forever were the Curiosities and Prodigies gathered in one tent so that you could stroll from one to another. The Bearded Lady, the Dog-Faced Boy and the Moss-Haired Girl. The Human Pin-Cushion. Albright the Skeleton. Hassan Ali, the Egyptian giant, 7 feet 11 inches tall; and Khusania, the Hindu dwarf, 22 inches high. Hermann, the Balloon-Chested Marvel. The Elastic

Right Between impressive-looking banks and offices the cattle stand at the Fair.

10

Man, pulling out handfuls of himself and letting it snap back into place. Rob Roy the Albino, continuously dislocating his shoulders and elbows. Lalloo, the Double-Bodied Hindu, 'a young man with an encumbrance in the shape of another imperfect body'. Miss Delphi, the Orange-Headed Dwarf ('very properly dubbed the "What is she?" on account of the curious structure of her head'). Oguri Kiba, 'an armless Japanese who makes pretty little knick-knacks by means of her feet' . . .

*   *   *

From time to time, Arthur and Harry and William Henry would walk up to see Owd Tim. Where the last houses petered out, a stony lane meandered along a knobbly hillside; on one hand lay hard fields; on the other, the rough moors began. Owd Tim lived alone in a little grey cottage, one room up and one down, with its weathered door opening on to the track and its back windows always darkened by the sloping bents and heather behind. Brown hens strutted carefully in and out, scratching in the wayside grass and, in summer, luxuriating in warm bowls of scooped dust. Around and above stretched a wide unbroken

sky, noisy with larks and curlews and shrill gulls flown scavenging inland.

Owd Tim had been born in the reign of King George IV and had lived and worked there at his handloom all his long life. Decade after decade, he had watched the town below grow blacker, its streets reaching steadily outwards up the hillsides and its horizons increasingly speckled with chimneys, towers and steeples. He had never seen the sea, or mountains, or a city. Just once he had ridden in a railway train. He betrayed neither interest nor curiosity in the changing world.

Nobody was certain of Owd Tim's exact age, although the old parish register's rusty copperplate recorded his baptism. His worn flannel shirts and corduroy trousers and waistcoats had moulded themselves to his hale old frame, and stained white whiskers encircled his ruddy wrinkled face. He washed himself every Sunday morning, and his only luxury was an occasional smoke from a pungent clay pipe. Porridge formed his staple diet, breakfast, dinner and supper, and smoky oat-bread hung here and there about his house. He always wore clogs, and in his younger days had enjoyed a reputation as a clog-dancer.

Owd Tim had never married; neither had his four brothers who had died respectively 42, 35, 17 and nine years ago. All his life—on tens of thousands of mornings—he had got up at dawn in summer, rather before in winter, to feed his hens and himself and to sit at his loom weaving in the upstairs room where his squalid bed shared a corner with lumber and bins of meal. He slept when the daylight faded, be that early or late according to the time of year. Once a week, he had shouldered his woven piece and tramped over the moors to Halifax market (it was in this connection, half a century ago, that he had sampled his single railway ride, but hadn't liked it and preferred to walk). In his youth and middle age, many small cottage weavers had made the same journey, talking as they went; but gradually they had gone into factories or had died, and now only Owd Tim survived.

He had not actually done much weaving for several years now—except when the photographers, journalists, museum curators, and enlightened teachers with their pupils came to watch him. You could buy postcards of him in all the neighbouring towns ('Owd Tim, the Last Handloom Weaver'), brown poses sitting working at his loom, bobbin-winding in the sunshine outside his door, taking his ease in his living-room, a small dusty den cluttered with heirlooms, oak chests, dressers, pots, plates, clocks that wouldn't go, empty bird-cages (for one of his long-dead brothers had kept singing birds). Hens shared his sagging armchairs, and in his untidy grate, all the year round, he burned peat.

The journalists liked to compare Owd Tim, in appearance, with

Right Owd Tim, the last of the handloom weavers.

sundry statesmen and bishops, the late Mr Gladstone being most frequently cited. By mammoth calculations they had managed to credit him with having, throughout his life, woven some 234,780 yards of cloth. He had, they assessed, pressed the treadles of his loom 540 million times! His thumb and fingers had worn deep imprints into his wooden sleyboard. One enterprizing museum curator had already bespoken most of the contents of his cottage, for after his death.

Owd Tim never understood what all the fuss was about. He had simply lived a life like many others, that was all. It was almost as though he still thought there were other men, just like himself, somewhere over the next hill, round the next bend of the track. Perhaps he never fully grasped the enormity of being a sole survivor.

CHAPTER TWO

ONE WAR AND TWO ROYAL OCCASIONS

During the autumn of 1899, newspapers, even the local ones, ran a crescendo of headlines ('Transvaal Crisis' . . . 'Boer Ultimatum'), culminating simply with 'The War'. Strange words entered the common vocabulary—Kraaipan Siding, Elandslaagte, Magersfontein, Tulana Hill—and everybody talked about The Front. The press was full of The Front, ministers preached and prayed about The Front, people passed round letters from soldiers they knew at The Front, young Regulars for the most part, striking an attitude out of shock and bravado:

'I never thought war was like this, but we are all right now; we have plenty of water and food but we cannot get any beer' . . . 'I have slept in the open a few times now, laid in mud, in torrents of rain, and slept like a top' . . . 'This lyddite shell that our artillery are using is something awful to watch it burst' . . . 'We were drinking water from a pool that we fished twenty-one dead Boers out of. It was pretty thick; but we have gone higher up stream, where the water is better' . . . 'When we retired I was left by myself behind a rock, and I could not get out, for the bullets were whizzing all around me and over my head. I did laugh to myself. Please send me some cigarettes' . . .

For Arthur and Harry and William Henry, war meant a simplified redeployment of their small finances. For one penny, at the time, the corner stationer's offered a vexing choice of purchases: a ball, a mirror, a fishing-net, a slate, a cannon, a pop-gun, a trumpet, a whistle, a fog-horn, a whip, a boat, a rattle, a hat, 50 marbles or ten superior glass ollies. Now, however, they simply bought buttons embellished with the portraits of generals, and their lapels glowered with stern, duty-doing Bullers and Frenches, Penn Symonses and Lord Methuens. For twopence, you could buy a tiny white-whiskered doll of Boer President Kruger, complete with a little coffin to shut him in; but it was more fun to go to the clay-pit and make your own model Kruger, blacking his face and sliding him into a match-box.

The Mayor had opened a Patriotic Fund in aid of soldiers' widows and dependants. From his villa in France, the worsted magnate who sometimes occupied the turretted pseudo-medieval castle beyond the town's genteel fringe, had sent £1,000. Some of the bigger mill-owners had subscribed £250 each, and benefit concerts and church offertories had been adding their smaller but no less enthusiastic quota for weeks. Enthusiastic, too, had been the cheering off of

15

Reservists and volunteer ambulancemen, and a few dashing troopers of the Imperial Yeomanry. At the turn of the year, and of the new century, it was learned that the local Volunteer Battalion of the Duke of Wellington's West Riding Regiment was to contribute 36 men to an Active Service Contingent.

More than double that number vied for a place. In the event, single men were selected, plus a few married men without children. They included Harry's brother Stanley. For a fortnight, the Active Service Volunteers enjoyed the best time of their lives. They were the centre of attention on War Sunday — 7 January 1900 — when they paraded at the Parish Church. Solid citizens presented them with pipes, tobacco, cigarettes, chocolate, socks, bars of soap. They were invited to dinners and speeches in a drill hall hung with flags. When they entrained for their Halifax depot on the first irrevocable step of their journey to South Africa, factories closed and the whole town saw them off.

It was a raw, drizzling mid-day. Arthur and William Henry, standing on a wall-top clinging to railings outside the Court House, looked over a pavement full of damp caps and shawls and waving hands as the Volunteers marched by. The Battalion band led, resplendent in scarlet, playing 'Soldiers of the Queen'. The Active Service Contingent, however, did not appear so instantly colourful, having been kitted out in khaki for The Front. They marched in their new greatcoats, with sloped rifles, their faces heroically moustached beneath their big khaki-covered helmets. Their Captain (whose father had a factory ten diplomatic miles away) carried his drawn sword at his right shoulder. Behind walked the Mayor, persistently out of step and at risk of getting trampled by the rubicund Colonel's horse (neither horse nor Colonel were going anywhere except the railway station) which lunged and swung, unnerved by the shouting crowds. The rest of the Battalion brought up the rear, but nobody paid much attention to them: all the excitement, the cries of 'good luck', centred on the 36 khaki men in the big helmets.

At the railway station, where Harry had a privileged view by virtue of his brother Stanley, the press was even greater. There had been an attempt to limit the sale of platform-tickets, but the place was crammed nevertheless, and businessmen for the 12.10 train to Bradford, unable to tear themselves away, had deliberately missed it and stayed. Deafening under the smutty glass roof, the band vied with noisy steam from the flag-bedecked train, whilst the station-master's fluttering white gloves strove in vain to bring order out of the last melée of farewells. When belatedly the train pulled away, it was to a climax of cheers, shouts, tears, and the band's big drum still steadily beating.

Rather less than five months later, safely arrived in South Africa,

Right Volunteers march away for the Boer War. The Active Service Contingent followed the band.

Private Stanley Riley died of enteric fever, without having seen a single combatant Boer.

Meanwhile, the town found occasions to celebrate. Jubilant bells rang repeatedly that February, when Kimberley and Ladysmith were relieved and the enemy General Cronjé surrendered at Paardeberg. But the great day came in May with the relief of plucky little Mafeking. All work stopped the instant the news arrived—it happened to be breakfast-time—and within minutes portraits of Colonel Baden-Powell (obviously ready in advance) appeared everywhere. People donned red, white and blue ribbons and rosettes, scarves, neckties, or khaki slouch hats tucked up at the side after the fashion of 'Our Gallant Hero of Mafeking'. That night, the Mayor and Town Councillors, preceded by the Volunteer Battalion band still playing the inevitable 'Soldiers of the Queen', walked in a body to the Football Field where ecstatic thousands watched a fireworks display. 'Long Live Baden-Powell', fizzed the grand set-piece.

A couple of evenings later, the children at the Mission Sunday School were treated to tea and buns, and the Minister spoke feelingly of the siege of Mafeking and 'the fine qualities which were to be found in the character of its defender'. The gallant Colonel, the Minister very properly opined, 'was an example worthy to be followed by all the young people present'.

*　　*　　*

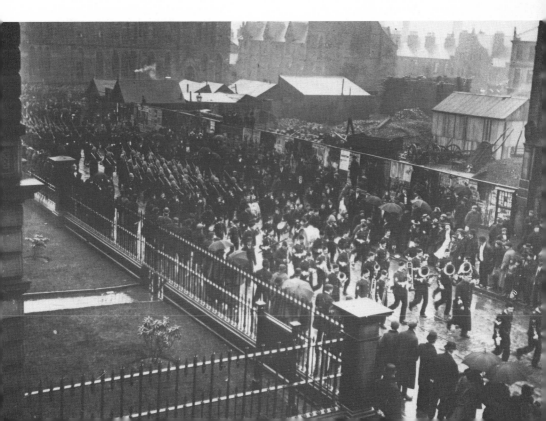

Tuesday 22 January 1901 was strangely muted. All day, a changing knot of people stood outside the Town Hall scrutinizing the bulletins as they were put up, fresh from Osborne House on the Isle of Wight, where the old Queen was very ill.

That evening, there was a lecture at the Mission, an eccentric middle-aged bachelor gentleman from the Cycling Club showing magic lantern slides on 'What I saw in Iceland'. The Minister, as chairman, opened with a prayer for the Queen—he had a friend on the Isle of Wight who had sent him a telegram saying: 'Situation very grave.' Nobody was able to concentrate on Iceland (pictures of harbours and snow and wooden buildings), and at 20 minutes past eight they heard a single Parish Church bell begin to toll, minus its normal jolly clangour, for it was muffled. Iceland was accordingly wound up very quickly, and the Minister, who had slipped briefly out at the first toll, informed them that the Queen had passed away at half past six. He was sure the news would cast a gloom over everybody, and they would all go home with sad hearts.

Not everybody possessed the will-power to go straight home. The Illingworths and the Berridges walked in a body to the Town Hall, where many were now gathered, to read the final bulletin. 'Her Majesty breathed her last', this said, 'surrounded by her children and grandchildren'. All the while, at long intervals, the single bell tolled.

It was a night of telegrams. From the local Member of Parliament, travelling abroad, came a curt instruction to the Mayor: 'Join national sorrow'—a superfluous advice, the Mayor having already telegraphed to Osborne House: 'Earnest prayers for your welfare'. Telegrams of condolence had also been dispatched by the Board of Guardians and the Co-operative Society. All over town, meetings had finished abruptly at 20 past eight.

For days, the death of the Queen overshadowed all else. Harry, selling newspapers, would remember for the rest of his life the heavy black borders round their front pages. Flags flew ostentatiously at half-mast. Whole streets drew their window-blinds as a mark of respect. Evenings were devoid of concerts and pie suppers, all postponed. On Sunday morning, the Minister preached on 'A Tribute to a Noble Memory' ('We are met under the shadow of a great sorrow. It is on occasions such as this that we are taught the utter poverty of words; our deepest needs and emotions find expression not in words, but in sighs and tears. The greatest Monarch that the world has ever seen has passed away, and the whole world is the poorer for it.'); in the evening, on 'The Subject's Duty to the King'.

On 2 February, the Queen was laid to rest and the new King was proclaimed. All the factories and shops closed for the day, few trains ran. The entire town packed the main street before the Court House, all wearing black, on a grey day; the only colours were the robes of the

Right King Edward VII is proclaimed king by the Mayor, 1901.

Mayor and Town Clerk as they stood above the throng, flanked by two scarlet Volunteer trumpeters.

The Town Clerk took a pace forward to the front of his platform: 'Oyez! Oyez! Oyez! Let all persons keep silence while there is read a letter from His Majesty's Most Honourable Privy Council'.

He stepped back, and the Mayor came forward: 'Whereas it has pleased Almighty God to call to His Mercy our late Sovereign Lady Queen Victoria, of Blessed and Glorious memory, by whose Decease the Imperial Crown of the United Kingdom of Great Britain and Ireland is solely and rightfully come to the High and Mighty Prince Albert Edward . . .'

Never before had Arthur seen so many tall black hats. The big gold Borough mace, held aloft, had black crêpe twined round and round its shaft. A drizzle was falling, penetrating and cold, but nobody stirred. The Mayor's voice, never strong, quivering now with a sense of the occasion, carried to the farthest edges of the still crowd. Thousands of faces listened, serious and attentive.

'. . . To whom we do acknowledge all Faith and constant Obedience with all hearts and humble Affection, beseeching God, by Whom Kings and Queens do reign, to bless the Royal Prince Edward the Seventh with long and happy Years to reign over Us.'

The trumpeters sounded a fanfare, heads turned to watch the Town Hall flag rise slowly to the top of its pole, three cheers for King Edward

VII brought the ceremony to a close. Leaving the rest of the day (a Saturday) with no work, no shopping, no sport, no entertainment. Luckily for some, the publicans had voted to stay open.

*   *   *

On Saturday 9 August 1902, everybody got up early, but the bell-ringers at the Parish Church were up even earlier, their peals fitfully jangling from the grey tower with its big red, white and blue flag. There were flags all over the town too, coloured strings of bunting, pictures of the King and Queen, and across the wide main street hung Chinese lanterns. Dark familiar walls took on a holiday flavour.

All the Nonconformists were having a united service at the great square Congregational Chapel, whither the Mission scholars walked in a body. Their Sunday School secretary had collected their Coronation medals from the Town Hall, and now he doled them out of a cardboard box — grey pewter discs on an inch of ribbon, bearing on one side King Edward and Queen Alexandra, and on the other the date and the name of the Mayor. Carefully, they pinned them into their coat-fronts.

The Congregational Chapel smelled heavily of polish and hot scrubbing-water. Arthur was unaccustomed to the weight of worshipping hundreds, their ponderous upsurge as they rose to sing, their loud subsidence as they sat to listen. The Minister, a black gesticulating beetle against the long silver organ-pipes, was plainly enjoying the occasion: 'The King has many characteristics which have made him popular with his people. He has never posed as a saint. He is no hypocrite. A certain writer said of him lately, "There is his sterling genuineness, his John Bull frankness, his freedom from all artificialities, his abhorrence of cant" . . .'

Bunting brightened the Chapel, draped from the gallery-rails, threaded among the organ-pipes. 'God Bless Our King and Queen!' the mottoes shouted from every surface. High behind the pulpit, a big weary portrait of King Edward half-smiled down upon the Minister: 'The joys and sorrows of the nation are focused in its Monarch. Every eye is upon him. He walks in the midst of that fierce light which beats upon a throne . . .'

When the mighty augmented choir rose up to sing the 'Hallelujah Chorus' (no need to practise, they'd been singing it every Christmas for life-times), it felt as if the echoing chapel roof was about to float away and reveal blue endless sky; whilst in its appreciative aftermath the Minister bobbed back more excited than ever: 'Let the bunting fly and the trumpet sound. Let festivity and rejoicing abound in our streets and homes. And whilst that brilliant pageant is being celebrated in the Metropolis, and the hearts of our countrymen are

Right *The Mission scholars portray Pope Gregory and the Saxon Children in the Coronation celebrations.*

being stirred with loyal fervour, let us sing as lustily as any, "God Save the King!" '

In the afternoon, very early, Arthur was in the wide enclosed railway yard where the Sunday Schools' procession of historical tableaux was forming up. Decorated waggons stood in rows, their sleek horses impatiently stamping heavy hooves and shaking great beribboned heads. Into one wheeled bower of grass and ferns clambered a white-robed and fiercely-bearded band of Druids . . . outside the wooden walls of Calais, Queen Philippa prepared to confront her chained burghers . . . a shoal of small boys in Lincoln green shouldered their longbows and pretended they were Robin Hood's Merrie Men . . . in a genteel open-air drawing-room, young Queen Victoria posed in a dressing-gown and waited for news of her accession . . . Sunday School after Sunday School, waggon after waggon, they bustled into fancy dress: Edward VI founding the Bluecoat School . . . Lady Jane Grey being offered the crown . . . Sir Francis Drake playing bowls . . . Britannia on a pedestal gazing forgivingly down on some kneeling Boers.

The Mission scholars, it had been (not altogether appropriately) decided, were to portray Pope Gregory and the Saxon Children. The latter, youngsters from the primary class, had been tied up in old rugs to look like skins, and a couple of the big girls, as Roman ladies, were able to flaunt their finery and giggle to their hearts' content. As one of Pope Gregory's retainers, Arthur was required simply to stand draped in velvet curtains, leaning on a staff and trying to look pensive. Everybody was in place much too early, listening apprehensively for the signal for the procession to start.

Outside in the streets, thousands of people were waiting too. Those within sight of the Mechanics' Institute balcony strained their eyes and ears in rapt concentration. 'The National Anthem', the Official Programme of Festivities had instructed, 'will be played once by the band, after which a slight pause will be made, and it is requested that after this pause the crowd be in readiness to take up the singing with the *down beat* of the Conductor's wand'. Three cheers for the King and Queen would follow.

In the railway yard, the rustling, shuffling waggons and the restless jingling horses waited, till at last they heard it over the roof-tops— 'God Save the King', louder than they had ever heard singing before. Almost according to plan came four rousing cheers (somebody had suggested an extra one for the Mayor), and then the great railway gates swung open and the tableaux procession lumbered out on to the rattling setts. In front of each waggon walked a boy dressed like a Medieval herald, carrying the title on a banner; at each horse's head came a carter in a clean white apron; and aboard each tableau the characters tried to hold their much-rehearsed poses against the unfamiliar movement of the waggons.

Arthur leaned determinedly on his staff. The little Saxon children pitched about (Pope Gregory, who seemed to have assumed some of the saintliness of his original, helped to steady them), and the Roman ladies giggled more than ever. Street by street, building by building, he watched the crowded town jostle slowly past.

He had never seen so many people. All along the pavements, schoolchildren had been assembled class by class: solid squares of girls in white dresses and black boots, of boys in black suits and white collars; bobbing seas of hats and caps, straw benjies, sailor hats, bonnets, glengarries; lady teachers elegant in lace and frills; sober men in tall silk hats and rounded billy-cocks; policemen with shining belt-buckles and dazzling white gloves. And behind, sitting along wall-tops with their legs dangling, rows of men and youths, and more occasional women with careful skirts. At all the windows above shops and banks, sharing the frontages with flags and bunting, heads craned; parents held their infants over sills. Beyond again, up the sidestreets, people perched on walls, held on to trees, stood up in carts. In one high five-storeyed mill due for demolition, precarious figures crammed behind every smashed window. Accumulated talking and pointing made a mighty stir.

Later in the afternoon there was tea at the Mission, followed by entertainments in the newly-mown Park, where the Mayor had planted a row of commemorative oaks. The Parish Church Athletic Club, clean and trim in white vests and trousers, went through their gymnastic paces, and the Three Zonells knocked one another about.

Right *The coronation medal these children wear seems to us to foretell other medals which many of these lads were to wear in the fateful years that lay ahead of them.*

All the while, bands played—as one tired, another took over. Daylight faded heavy with a scent of crushed grass; and the crowds moved on to admire the Town Hall and the Mechanics' Institute—even the foundations of the new Public Library—lit by hundreds of coloured electric lamps. 'Long Live Our King and Queen!' shone the lights across the front of the Town Hall.

But in the gathering dusk Arthur joined a ceaseless hurrying column climbing the road up to Wood Top. Bonfires had been built on most of the hills, but this was the one for which the carts of the Sanitary Inspector had been toiling for days. That morning's newspaper had recited statistics: 123 feet high, 47 feet round at the base, weight 70 tons approximately. Contents: 84 old barrels, 150 skeps, 150 trees varying in circumference from a foot to a yard, four tons of oil and tar. The whole liberally dowsed with paraffin.

A great crowd surrounded the bonfire, tense in the darkness, keeping a respectful distance because, it was said, thousands of rats infested it. In the whispering, shifting gloom, mothers held their children closer, fathers lifted sons and daughters on to their shoulders. The Sanitary Inspector himself, gingerly clutching a torch on the end of a long pole, clambered several yards up a ladder, touched the highest point with his flame and scurried quickly down. The crowd shrank instinctively back as the bonfire leapt roaring ablaze. Shielding his face with a scorching hand, Arthur watched fascinated. Not a single rat ran out.

Below *Coronation celebrations, 1902.*
'84 old barrels, 150 skeps, 150 trees . . .' went into the town's coronation bonfire.

CHAPTER THREE

MESSRS ELI WADSWORTH AND SONS

When Arthur was 11 years old, he became the doubtful possessor of a Labour Certificate. This rather daunting document ('In the case of any child commencing as a half-timer before obtaining this Certificate, the Parent becomes liable to immediate prosecution without further notice') testified that Arthur Illingworth, of Peel Place, was not less than 11 years of age, as appeared by his Registrar's Certificate of Birth; further, that according to one of Her Majesty's Inspectors of Schools he had reached the 4th Standard (' "reached" means passed in reading, writing, and arithmetic, in the standard mentioned'). Signed by the headmaster and the Clerk to the School Board, the Labour Certificate ('This Certificate Must Be Very Carefully Preserved') permitted him to be employed by Messrs Eli Wadsworth and Sons as a half-timer. This meant that, on the first and third weeks of each month, he would work mornings and attend school in the afternoons; and on the alternate weeks, work afternoons and go to school in the mornings.

Arthur's mother was not especially happy about this arrangement, but the majority of the older Board School boys and girls—including Arthur's sister who would shortly reach 13 and begin working full-time—were, through custom and economic necessity, involved in the half-time factory system. Only a very few parents (like William Henry's) were able to keep their children at school all day.

Messrs Eli Wadsworth and Sons, worsted spinners and manufacturers, occupied five-storey Providence Mills whose lines of throbbing windows lit wintry dawns and dusks with a bright and merry rhythm. In one or another of their departments, Messrs Eli Wadsworth and Sons employed more than a thousand people. Arthur's sister worked there, as his mother had done before her marriage. Blunt old Eli, it was said, knew every worker by name. By boldness, flair and luck, he had built himself up from nothing, and still, at the age of 78, came into the mill most days. His sons were more businesslike and less familiar—one served as a magistrate and the other had been Mayor—but kept a number of faithful old workers on their payroll long after their usefulness had ceased. The firm enjoyed a solid reputation throughout the worsted trade.

Not that such considerations softened the reality of Arthur's first half-day at Providence Mills. He started at six o'clock on a January morning. It had snowed in the night, latterly turning to a sleety rain. A piercing breeze stirred round corners. Under the gas-lamps, the streets shone running wet over sheeted ice; furrows of pocked dwindling snow clung under walls. With his breakfast-tin under his arm, one hand deep in his pocket and the other clutching at gates, railings, anything that offered support, Arthur shuffled cautiously downhill; his sister Connie, very superior as befitted her age and experience, chivvied him along. All around them in the darkness, hurrying figures tended in a common direction, clogs clumping and slipping. At this stage in the day, there was no conversation.

By contrast, Messrs Eli Wadsworth and Sons was warm and cheerful. A bemused Arthur was taken, ten minutes early, into what seemed an enormous spinning department, pungent with smells of gas and grease and wool, the rows of frames still large complicated shadows. A man with a long taper went round lighting scores of faintly-glimmering gas mantles. The women and girls who were arriving, faces red from the cold outside, seemed preoccupied in ranging their enamel tea and cocoa cans (breakfast would be at eight) along the steam pipes to be warming up—indeed, Arthur's first distinct job would be to fetch hot water to brew up from the boiler-house. At six precisely, the factory leapt into light and noise: the frames burst into rhythmic motion and the dim gas mantles came fully aglow.

During the next months, this chattering, rotating place, where thousands of rovings converted endlessly into yarn, entered into Arthur's very bones and being. For a while he was a doffer, scurrying about removing filled bobbins and replacing them with empties. He was shown the rudiments of cleaning the frames. He was put with a spinner who taught him how to twist broken threads together (for they were always breaking), and he became a piecer—in that district it was customary to add an extra syllable and say piecener! He learned to walk instinctively, without flinching, up and down the loud vibrating aisles; to converse, without shouting, by watching his workmates' lips move; to time his morning entrance neatly with the warning outburst of the factory buzzer. Within a few weeks, school had become the more irksome half of the day.

Harry was doffing and piecening in the same shed, although for Harry the shift from school to work was a slight one: he had been working for years, as an errand-boy in the evenings and selling newspapers, and his school attendances had always been worse than average. Harry's introduction to Messrs Eli Wadsworth and Sons had seemed, however, the more traumatic because it followed immediately upon the best week he had ever had. To wit, the Cinderella Club took an interest in Harry.

The Cinderella Club was an undenominational group of citizens whose aim was simply, by public subscription, 'to ameliorate the conditions of the poorest children in the town'. Each day they served a

Right *'Half-timers' wait around the factory gate.*

26

free dinner, of which Harry had from time to time partaken; and in summer, in segregated batches of 30, they sent boys or girls for a week's holiday at their camp over in Lancashire, on Morecambe Bay.

The Cinderella Club's camp consisted of a large wooden hut with a corrugated-iron roof. Some swings adjoined, and a cricket pitch (when girls were in residence, the latter had other, more feminine uses). The food was plain but wholesome, and plenty of it; the blankets on each of the 30 iron bedsteads brightly coloured; the matron strict but capable; and one or another gentleman or lady forever dropping in to help with fun and games. Harry treasured every single minute of his week. The sun shone every day from a blue lucid sky. Behind the camp rose a low limestone hill covered in straggly woods, whilst in front, level turf stretched away to the sea. If you

walked straight forward—as Harry did, every day—you went on and on over short grass dotted with warm salty pools and cropped by clean white sheep (which trotted bawling inland of their own accord, in hundreds, just before dusk), till you came to hard sand grooved and patterned by the sea.

*   *   *

Meanwhile, William Henry passed an examination to the Trade and Grammar School, and his parents (unlike the parents of many promising scholars) were able and willing to let him continue his studies. Henceforth, he carried a bagfull of homework back and forth, morning and evening, and the fronts of his exercise books were embellished with an engraving of the school and its handsome clock-tower. Very suddenly, William Henry's surroundings expanded into new undreamed-of vistas. The Trade and Grammar School boasted strange-smelling laboratories for chemistry and physics; masters wearing black gowns taught French and German and Latin, Greek even, and the higher mysteries of mathematics; whilst a regular trickle of older boys—veritable young men, with moustaches—won County Council Scholarships to colleges and universities.

Spare-time clubs flourished: Rugby and Association football, rambling, cycling, photography, cricket—the latter played an annual match against the Girls' Grammar School, the boys being expected to bat, ball and field left-handed ('This arrangement', the school magazine tartly observed, 'generally results in a feminine victory'). These did not unduly interest William Henry, but the school play, 'Hamlet', did; as also a Debating Club which argued such daring subjects as 'The Settlement of the Land Question' and 'Has Great Britain reached the Zenith of Her Power?' William Henry shyly put in a word on the latter (he thought Great Britain had).

Out in the workaday world, as the years slipped by, Arthur finished with school altogether and grew familiar with Messrs Eli Wadsworth and Sons who, realising that he was a sharp, dependable lad, introduced him by degrees to their different processes. So Arthur came steadily to understand wool's epic journey from sheep to fabric; seeing how, newly unloaded, still stuck with burrs and dung and daubed with farmers' tar markings, the fleeces began with the woolsorters, deft with their cutting shears, filling their wicker baskets with varying qualities—from prized picklock (best wool from neck and shoulders, ribs and back) down a descending scale through prime, choice, super (all good, from thighs, haunches and tail), to middling head and inferior downrights, seconds, abb, livery and short coarse (worst of all, from belly and lower legs).

He watched the wool being harrassed into less recognizable shapes:

Right A wool-sorting room.

beaten to extract dirt and twigs; washed and boiled, dragged at with automatic forks, subjected to soap and lather and steam, transformed to a spotless white; dried and oiled; carded, shaken at speed from one toothed cylinder to another to become a dainty white film; passed through gill-boxes, fibres smoothed into parallel directions; combed with rhythmic teeth of steel, unfolded into silky slivers; spun, converted to yarn, dyed and woven, burled and mended ... The complex worsted manufacture had, by Messrs Eli Wadsworth and Sons, been reduced to one continuous and seemingly effortless process.

The trade employed its own terse jargon, of Lincoln Hogs and South Down, Midland Counties and Botany, with more than a hint of the exotic. At one time and another, the world came into Providence and its sister-mills: mohair from Turkey and the Cape, alpaca from Peru; wools from Persia, Egypt, the East Indies, Syria; Russian cashmere and Chinese camel-hair; goat-hair from Tunis and the Mediterranean. Therein, danger lay. Sometimes in stained foreign fleeces lurked unseen the deadly spores of anthrax—'the woolsorters' disease', although it could strike anyone involved with wool. Workers felt inexplicable pains in their back and chest, breathed with difficulty, came over exhausted and died within hours. Or they developed sudden malignant blisters, swelled and died with poisoned blood. In Bradford, an Anthrax Investigation Board was grappling with the problem, as yet in vain.

When old Eli Wadsworth was 80, he threw a colossal tea-party for his employees who, by dint of careful packing, were accommodated

for the occasion in the Volunteers' Drill Hall. They had collected for a birthday present, a solid silver rose bowl suitably inscribed; and when the old man stood up to thank them, with genuine tears on his cheeks, he spoke of 'his deep interest in the welfare of those who served him'. This was no empty form of words: beyond the spruce efficiency of Providence Mills lay such details as the young workers' sick club — boys and girls paid a half-penny a week and received, when ill, half-a-crown a week — and Wadsworths' Brass Band, which played mightily at concerts and galas; it was old Eli who watched out for likely players and provided the instruments and a room at his residence to practise in. The main 1,200 horse-power engine at Providence Mills had, with due ceremony on its inauguration, been named 'Sophia' after the late Mrs Eli Wadsworth (two smaller engines were called 'Alice' and 'Lucy' after his daughters). In the engine-room, old Eli kept a table and chair, part of his original furniture when he had married and set up house 56 years before. Often he could be seen there, sitting in the chair, his elbows on the table, lost in thought and reminiscence listening to 'Sophia's' steady throbbing. The firm's oversight of Arthur was entirely typical: irrevocably, once his knowledge of machinery and human nature had developed to the requisite standard, he was in the fullness of time made an overlooker.

Meanwhile, life was changing in many directions. Amongst the horse-traffic, as the young century advanced, uncertain new motor-cars were increasingly seen. The Town Council electrified their tramways, auctioning off their weather-beaten old cars and patient clopping horses, and converting their stables into a depot and workshops. Arthur's father, whose cab had lately represented a declining livelihood, took the opportunity of training as the driver of a gleaming open-topped tram smartly painted in crimson and white. His hours remained long and unsociable, and he stood exposed to the elements; but his wage was assured and the Corporation provided him with a waterproof overcoat and a cap. He was instructed to sound his bell as little as possible when passing churches and chapels on Sundays. The electric trams, efficient and punctual, heralded the end of the old horse and cattle fairs by pushing them ignominiously into the side streets — tramlines and a regular service precluded standing livestock in the main thoroughfares.

Ironically the public, on the threshold of mechanized road transport, had an exuberant fling at travelling under their own efforts, as cycling and walking attained the proportions of crazes. Clubs of men in stiff collars and women in divided skirts pedalled sedately out along country lanes; the timid and the elderly rode tricycles, whilst young racing bloods broke speed records. Walking matches too became the order of the day. Contestants in dozens and scores stepped

Above right *A sedate form of early tricycle.*

Below right *The start of the walking match.*

30

briskly out from Bradford to York (39½ miles), from Manchester to Halifax (32 miles), from Leeds to Pontefract and back (27 miles), up and down and round and across Ilkley Moor. No sports and gala was complete without its walkers, feted at public-houses en route, cheered on from the roadsides, the winners played home with brass bands.

Harry, in his late teens, enjoyed a summer of glory as a walker (Harry, already moving aimlessly from job to job, from factory to foundry to navvying and back again to factory; already embarked on casual relationships, already arguable father of a child born to a neighbouring girl in the Ginnel; soon to receive several cautions and a summons for drunk and disorderly conduct). In one glorious summer of pounding feet and swinging elbows, Harry won two cups, a carving-knife, three bottles of whisky and an inscribed tobacco-jar! Briefly he became a familiar name in the local newspaper: 'H. Riley walked magnificently, and during the latter stages of the contest attained a speed of about six miles an hour, while his average rate for the whole distance was 5½ miles an hour . . .'

Every year, for a few days towards the end of July—the local 'Tide'—most factories stopped. Messrs Eli Wadsworth and Sons were amongst a growing number of firms who gave a full week's holiday (some resumed work on the Wednesday or Thursday), although their workers had to budget carefully for a week without wages, to say nothing of extra expenses. The summer he was 20, Arthur and two others from the Young Men's Mutual Improvement Class went up the Dale, where the Co-operative Holidays Association had opened one of its centres. They caught the train through green hills to its farthest station, then wheeled their luggage in a bright orange handcart (the previous week's holidaymakers had just used it to push *their* luggage stationwards) along winding lanes between white stone walls.

The holiday centre was a big wooden bungalow with a long verandah, in a field beside the brown river. Its founder, a former Congregational minister in Lancashire, had a shining ideal of healthy outdoor holidays for rich and poor alike. Everybody staying there—mainly a mixture of clerks, artisans and teachers in families and groups—would join in together to make one happy convivial company. 'A bright-coloured tie', Arthur had been advised on booking, 'adds to the cheerfulness of the party'. They would rise early to fetch milk and eggs from the nearby stone farm, would bathe in the river and drink from cold streams. By day they would go for walks, exploring the surrounding Dale and learning of its geology and birds and wild flowers. In the evenings they would hold debates, would listen to lectures, dance and play games. There would be picnic meals in the wide-open air, and summer nights of singsongs round a campfire under the clear stars. Some of these things did indeed

Right Ladies to the left, gentlemen to the right—Edwardian ramblers at Jennet's Foss in Malhamdale.

happen, and all of them would have, but for the weather. After the first Sunday, it rained the whole week, blotting out the hills in grey murk, turning the field-paths into standing water. Afterwards, Arthur returned home muddy but stimulated.

*   *   *

So Arthur started spasmodically attending meetings of the Independent Labour Party, the local branch of which had some rather grubby club-rooms and a terse and forthright statement of objects, namely: 'The collective ownership and control of the means of production, distribution, and exchange. All operations to be carried on irrespective of the convenience of other political parties or organisations.' Members—the sort of people Arthur had met on

holiday—paid a penny a week. The Independent Labour Party ran a cycling club, a camera club and a glee club; held picnics, concerts and musical evenings; maintained a reading-room bursting with propaganda. On Sunday afternoons they held a Socialist Sunday School, and on Sunday evenings there were lectures. Honorary Lectures Secretary was William Henry Berridge.

William Henry had done very well at the Trade and Grammar School; he had passed examinations, won scholarships, been away to college in London and come back again as a Secondary School teacher. He wore spectacles, fidgetted a good deal, was seldom seen to smile. His nervous enthusiasm kept those Sunday evening lectures going. Week after week, he would rise behind his table to introduce an intense visiting speaker: 'The March of the Machine' ('The speaker traced the progress of the machine from its inception', William Henry wrote up the weekly *Clarion* paragraph, 'and showed what a blessing it would be if it was owned by the many instead of the few') . . . 'Socialism: the Only Way' . . . 'Women and Socialism' . . . 'Socialism and Waste' . . . 'Socialism and the Unemployed' . . . 'What is Socialism?' . . . 'Socialism—What It Is, and Is Not' . . . Keir Hardie and Philip Snowden had been to lecture, but that was before William Henry's time.

Then, quite unexpectedly, Sir James died. Aged 83, Sir James had been Liberal Member of Parliament for nearly 20 unbroken years. He had been in local politics all his life, had been Mayor three times, was a Freeman of the Borough and a Justice of the Peace. An industrialist, thousands of workpeople had passed through his employ, and he had tried to serve what he regarded as their best interests. A Nonconformist, there were few local chapels which had not gained by his benefactions. A traveller, the town affectionately claimed he had once brought two crocodiles back from the Holy Land and kept them in his mill-dam! An amateur geologist, he had read frequent papers at the Mechanics' Institute and the Natural History Society. 'He had no gifts of eloquence, and public speaking was not his forte', the press gravely penned his epitaph, 'but his foresight, his strong common sense, his extensive knowledge of commerce and the methods of business, and his great industry, made him of far more than ordinary value in the many departments of public life with which he was concerned'. His son, produced from the same mould and confident of the working-class vote, was standing in the subsequent by-election.

The next month was frantically busy. The Conservatives naturally produced their candidate, but so, for the first time, did the Independent Labour Party, though they had to bring one in from Birmingham—a solicitor every inch as gentlemanly as his opponents. For four weeks William Henry hardly had time to sleep, what with organizing and canvassing; the club-rooms hummed with activity every night. Big rowdy meetings were held, at which candidates publicly debated such topics as tariff reform, home rule, land tax and the National Insurance Bill—much of it over the heads of their audiences, who had come mainly for the excitement and to heckle. The Birmingham solicitor's stylish wife probably did most for her husband's cause by getting herself photographed talking to some ragged children.

Election day—the town's first with three parties—was far and away the liveliest anybody could remember. People sported coloured rosettes of yellow or blue (not so many red), and tied them on their horses and dogs. The Liberals had distributed thousands of buttons bearing portraits of the late Sir James and his son. All the schools were closed for the day, and gangs of children went about cheering and booing the beribboned carriages and motor cars ferrying voters to the polls, grimy labourers and quarrymen covered in stone-dust riding, for this one day, in unaccustomed grandeur. The Independent Labour Party had few motor cars and not many traps, but their supporters, it was suspected, 'were making use of any vehicle that came their way'. Outlying cottagers were walking up to six miles each way to cast their votes, and one Liberal gentleman, aged 80, died of a heart attack whilst cycling into town.

LABOUR UNION

MEETS IN THE

CO-OPERATIVE HALL, QUEEN ST.,

On SUNDAY EVENINGS at 6-30.

SUNDAY, NOVEMBER 25th, 1894.

SPEAKER:

FRED BROCKLEHURST, B.A.

(MANCHESTER). SUBJECT:

"A LIVING WAGE."

Vocalist: MR. W. LEACH,

OF KEIGHLEY.

Chairman: MR. E. HORNER.

LADIES INVITED. QUESTIONS. COLLECTION.

That night, nobody went to bed. Men who had to be getting ready for work by half past five the following morning declared that they were staying up to wait for the result. This was duly announced from the Mechanics' Institute balcony at 40 minutes after midnight, but the noisy crowds couldn't hear it. However, some ingenious official had thought of that, and a strategically-placed magic lantern threw the figures hugely against the Institute wall:

'Liberal: 4,667
Conservative: 3,842
Labour: 3,452.'

Amid the answering hubbub, William Henry reflected that his party, albeit bottom of the poll, had become a force to be reckoned with.

Nor was it the only movement in the ascendant. The Suffragettes too were on the march. About this time came members of the Women's Social and Political Union to hold a public meeting. They booked the largest hall in town. Four of the ladies had been ejected from various buildings up and down the country, including the Houses of Parliament, and had suffered imprisonment for their agitations on behalf of votes for women. Their visit aroused considerable interest and the hall was filled, the audience, while mainly of women, being strongly leavened with curious and facetious men.

It had been arranged that a few sympathetic officials from the Independent Labour Party should sit on the platform with the Suffragettes (whom most men referred to as the Shrieking Sisters), and William Henry, not without trepidation, took a seat. The meeting lasted for over two hours, running a gamut of moods. There were a few male hecklers, and a row of boisterous younger men who kept singing 'Put Me Amongst the Girls'; there were strident, spirited, indignant and humorous speeches, with heavy references to 'His Majesty's hotel at Holloway'; there was some applause and rather more laughter; but, above all, there were telling word-pictures of women sewing sacks at three-halfpence a dozen and baby bonnets at twopence each, toiling 13 hours a day for six shillings a week, leaving their offspring while they went into the mills, and a doctor at Blackburn who was allegedly suggesting 'that cradles ought to be allowed in the factories so that little children could be attended by their own mothers'. Declared one lady (and by now the row of young men had been silenced): 'Criminals, paupers, lunatics and women have no vote.'

A few weeks later, while Sir James's son happened to be attending a function at the Town Hall, a local Suffragette chained and padlocked herself to some railings—unfortunately, the nearest were three

Right The Independent Labour Party candidate and his wife strike an appropriate pose.

streets away, which somewhat spoiled her effect. Since she had thrown the key down a grate, she could not be removed immediately, and a crowd had ample time to gather. And all the while, as policemen fished down the grate and sawed clumsily at her chain, she kept on shouting 'Votes for women! Votes for women!' surrounded by laughter and abuse.

*   *   *

The last time Arthur and Harry and William Henry met all three together was quite by chance, in 1913 when, as local tradition would subsequently phrase it, 'the aeroplane landed'. To be precise, this was a tractor biplane on a flight from Aldershot to Scotland when its pilot, an Army captain, happened to run short of petrol and landed in the first flattish field he came across. Petrol was obligingly rushed up by motor car, but the weather meanwhile deteriorated and the pilot

(suitably wined and dined in the nearest gentleman's residence) decided to stay the night. Since it was a Saturday, and since a War Office regulation forbade Army machines from flying on Sundays, the biplane remained in the field for nearly two days.

Absolutely everybody walked up to have a look at it. Arthur and Harry and William Henry went on the Sunday afternoon, by which time the biplane stood roped off in a corner (earlier comers had been able to touch it, and some had even managed to write their signatures on its wings and fuselage). Its propeller-blades had been wrapped in linen bags. The farmer was charging a penny admission into his field!

Below *The biplane is helped into the air.*

CHAPTER FOUR

PLAYING THE GAME

A careful reader of the newspapers in 1914 would have noted, on 28 June, the assassination of an Austrian Archduke in Sarajevo, followed by some weeks of mounting international unpleasantness. Most ordinary working-folk, however, bound up within their personal routines and commitments, were not especially interested; so that the headlines early in August—'War in Europe'—came like the proverbial bolt from the blue.

An atmosphere of strained excitement veered at times towards panic. Housewives, in dread of famine, scurried from shop to shop, hoarding foodstuffs: prices rose. Boy Scouts and Water Committee employees stood nightly guard over reservoirs, lest enemy agents poison them (a German disguised as a woman had, it was rumoured, been cycling about the district enquiring as to their locations). Several local residents of foreign origin were arrested on 8 August and apologetically released on 9 August. Officials from the War Office arrived buying up horses and motor vehicles; the Mayor formed a War Relief Committee; and recruiting began immediately.

Reservists were recalled and speeding on their way within hours of the announcement of hostilities (two local deserters, even, gave themselves up to go on active service). Territorials likewise mobilized, camped briefly in schools, and were gone. But these were not enough. Lord Kitchener appealed for a whole New Army—'Your King and Country Need You!' was his slogan—and young men, who had hitherto been considered eminently undistinguished, acquired a sudden desirability. Drums and bugles of military bands stirred the blood. At Bradford, they were raising a Pals' Battalion: 'Play the Game!' their posters exhorted, mustering 'dashing forwards' (their full-back was Lord Kitchener, their three-quarter backs General French, Admiral Jellicoe, Lord Fisher and General Smith-Dorrien). In Leeds, an illuminated tram sparkled with the admonition: 'Nah Then, John Willie, Ger Agate, Lad, an' Join t'Army'.

One evening Arthur attended a recruiting meeting. The hall was packed, the platform solid with Town Councillors, mill-owners, clergymen. Only a prospective Parliamentary Labour candidate, nagged by doubts, had tendered his apologies for absence.

'Britain is at death grips with the greatest tyrant of all times; a human monster who, while assuming love and affection for his people, is prepared to sacrifice a million of their lives and render thousands of homes desolate in order to assuage his avaricious and wicked desires.' A Councillor was speaking, but it could equally have been a clergyman, or a mill-owner, or any one of them.

39

'We have been forced into this war to do what is right and honourable and what we believe to be our duty'—this was the main point over which the Labour candidate had stumbled—'and I hope that we shall not depart from this purpose until we have achieved our object and broken down and trampled underfoot the destructive and tyrannical power which, through wanton destruction alone, has made miserable and desolate thousands of homes throughout Europe . . .'

"KEIGHLEY LADS, PLAY THE GAME!"

2nd Bradford   **Pals' Battalion**

Full Back:
LORD KITCHENER.

Three Quarter Backs:
General FRENCH.   **Admiral JELLICOE.**
LORD FISHER.   **General SMITH DORRIEN.**

Half Backs:
Gen. Sir DOUGLAS HAIG.   **Admiral BEATTY.**

WANTED AT ONCE
DASHING FORWARDS
FOR THE KEIGHLEY COMPANY.

Apply for all Particulars:
RECRUITING OFFICE:—DRILL HALL, KEIGHLEY.

The speeches continued for a long while, endlessly repeating and elaborating a single theme ('women have been ravished, innocent children slain, old men done to death, sacred and historical buildings ruthlessly destroyed'), but it was vouchsafed the Mayoress, the only woman speaker and taking a different tack, to raise the roof with thunderous applause and cheers: 'There are Yorkshire women as well as Yorkshire men, and I can assure the lads left behind that they will get nothing like the welcome, when the struggle is over, that will be

Left *Recruiting poster for the Bradford Pals Battalion.*

Below *Recruiting poster for the Duke of Wellington's Regiment.*

6th RESERVE BATTALION
DUKE OF WELLINGTON'S REGIMENT.

1,000 MEN
WANTED IMMEDIATELY.

FOR THE ABOVE BATTALION. ALL MEN TO SOLDIER TOGETHER.

UPHOLD THE HONOUR OF YOUR TOWN
COME AND SERVE NOW.

YORKSHIRE with it: broad acres, dense population and strapping sons, must not lag behind in this life and death struggle against the German military despot.

Your HOME, your WIFE, your MOTHER, your CHILDREN, your FUTURE, your EXISTENCE, depend on your decision. RECRUITS are needed urgently. Don't wait for your neighbour—set him an example. JOIN AT ONCE. Step into the ranks of those who are defending our shores before it is too late.

Remember the horrors of German Savagery in Belgium to men, women and children. Now is the time to put an end to this for all time. You must help if we are to emerge successfully, and AT ONCE, as delay will be fatal.

Terms of Enlistment:—4 years Home Defence, but a man of the Territorial Force must subject himself to liability to serve in any place outside the United Kingdom in the event of National Emergency. Men will be allowed to take their discharge at the termination of the War.

Apply :—DRILL HALL.

HELP OTHERS. HELP YOURSELF.

: GOD SAVE OUR KING AND EMPIRE. :

Edward Foulds & Sons, Printers, &c., Excelsior Works, Bingley.

41

given by the girls to those who have been to the war. When I see an able-bodied, well-built young man walking about the streets enjoying himself, I am ashamed of him.'

Arthur was not amongst those who surged forward to enlist; although Harry, he noticed, was—Harry, his work unexciting, his home squalid, his relations with young women complex, his prospects commonplace. Harry (who still daydreamed about his boyhood week on Morecambe Bay) was about to strike out on a new adventure.

A large batch of recruits left almost at once. Arthur, going along in his dinner-hour to watch them muster in the Town Hall Square, and to give Harry the luxury of a couple of cigars, was heavily reminded of those other men marching off nearly 15 years ago; and of Private Stanley Riley who had not come back. This time was quite different. This time, it was a tranquil late summer's day, with a hint of autumn in the air and the background hills subtly aglow. This time, the Town Hall Square was filled with nervy young men in their suits and newly-shined Sunday boots. More kept arriving from outlying villages, some in motor buses, others by a process proudly described as 'marching', but which Army sergeants would very shortly be blasphemously smartening up.

This time, the atmosphere was of an overall fragile cheerfulness, within which individuals—if left to themselves—lapsed into thoughtful silences. Recruiting officers chivvied the young men into rows: they stood up very straight, their hands at their sides. They had each been given, and had put on, an armband inscribed 'Kitchener's Man'; also a blanket (donated by a patriotic ladies' committee), which some rolled and tied 'en banderole' as they had seen Regular soldiers do. Well-wishers passed among them, doling out gifts. Somebody had brought a hamper of lucky white heather and stuck a sprig into the cap or the jacket of each young man. Other substantial gentlemen and ladies gave out tobacco, chocolate, even 'housewives' friends' containing needles, pins, cotton and buttons. These the young men stowed sheepishly into their pockets.

Inevitably came speeches about answering the call to duty, and there was an attempt to start hymn-singing, but few joined in. Arthur had delivered his cigars to a brittle, cocky Harry (bound today for Halifax and tomorrow Surrey, far away on the other side of London), and he had to get back to work. So he missed the grand march to the railway station, although he did hear a brass band, which had discovered a new tune called 'It's a Long, Long Way to Tipperary'.

*   *   *

As that 1914 summer deepened into autumn, war increasingly affected the town. In October the first Belgian refugees arrived, 50 of

Right Patriotic seriousness on the faces of young recruits.

them comprising several large families, surrounded by bags and bundles and carrying two babies. Boy Scouts had been meticulously briefed to attend to their luggage; and outside a reception centre in the Wesleyan Sunday School, children shouted a rehearsed 'Vive la Belgique!' A Refugee Committee had found rent-free houses, furniture, clothes; the local newspaper was persuaded to print a weekly summary of events in Flemish. The Belgians, it was thought, would only be here for, at most, a few months, as the war would soon be over.

Then there was the disgraceful affair of Mr Schulz, Mr Schneider and Mr Hofmann. For decades, these entirely respectable German-born gentlemen had kept butchers' shops in the town. Mr Schneider sang in the Glee Union, and Mr Hofmann's three sons had all passed with distinction through the Trade and Grammar School. Unfortunately, latish in the evening of a long tense Saturday, a gang of local louts decided to liven things up. They started at Mr Hofmann's. At the first tinkle of breaking glass, as at an arranged signal, the whole town seemed to go mad, and, within minutes, some thousands of people were milling about the streets. After they had smashed and looted Mr Hofmann's, they surged on to Mr Schneider's (an adjoining pawnshop being similarly mistreated), then to Mr Schulz's. Mr Schulz had taken the precaution of displaying his naturalization certificate in his shop-window, but this didn't save him, and bricks thrown through his upstairs windows just missed his child's cot.

All told, it was the most disgusting spectacle Arthur had ever seen: grown men kicking pies and loaves about like footballs, and a big woman from the Ginnel—whose face he had known all his life— cackling as she bore off some stolen weighing-scales. Then Arthur hurried home, escaping the reading of the Riot Act, the howled-down

appeals to reason of a Catholic priest, and the ultimate police baton charge (they had to wait till they got reinforcements from Bradford and Leeds) which cleared the town centre, messily, at a cost in broken heads.

But, on the whole, the war seemed not noticeably to affect Arthur. To be sure, Messrs Eli Wadsworth and Sons were busier than ever, working day and night on a big government contract for khaki cloth, but Arthur held aloof from the young men still flocking to the colours. Recruiting, indeed, was given a righteous boost just before Christmas, when German battle cruisers shelled Hartlepool, Scarborough and Whitby. 'Many thanks, Von Tirpitz', sneered the press. 'You bagged some eighty-odd civilians, a church and two ruins, we get about two new army corps.' And the posters: 'Men of Yorkshire! Help to Avenge the Murder of Innocent Women and Children! Join the New Army!' Entire football teams joined up, and a Parish Church Bible Class, complete with the curate.

From Harry in training came an enthusiastic letter: 'It is wonderful how all the recruits are getting into the way of things. Everyone seems to put his heart into the work. Our chief lesson is a lecture on the rifle by an expert. We have one hour of this each day. We have five hours marching, varied with cross-country running, squad drill, gymnastic exercises, football, and various other exercises, all of which' (for Harry had caught the mood of the moment) 'tend to make one a skilled soldier capable of doing useful work in the defence of one's country if needed.' His entire intake, he added, had volunteered for service overseas.

Presently, there were no longer enough men at home. Postwomen appeared on the rounds, and girl telegraph messengers. When a munitions factory was started, most of its workers were women. Arthur's sister's husband had enlisted, and his mother looked after their little girl while Connie went to work there. Her hours were long, sometimes she worked day shifts, sometimes night. She adapted quickly to a new life. She came home tired, she worried about her husband, but at the same time she found a cameraderie she had missed since her marriage. Indeed, the munitions factory seemed, to Connie and her workmates, vastly more stimulating than textiles had been, an oily masculine world of grinders, drills and pulleys, machines for sawing and milling, buffing and polishing, lathes for screwcutting, sliding, surfacing. Girls and women spoke easily of 18-pound high-explosive shells, of $3 \cdot 7$ in howitzers. They wore brown practical belted overalls, pushing their hair up under matching caps: little groups of special friends had their photographs taken in uniform, against inappropriate studio backdrops of painted woodlands and Grecian urns. They acquired a repertoire for sing-songs:

Right 'Every Man his Chance': Lord Derby, Director-General of Recruiting, outlining his scheme in 1915, paves the way for conscription.

44

> *Oh my heart is beating lightly,*
> *For I know I'm doing rightly*
> *When I'm turning out the shells to smash the Hun;*
> *And a melody comes ringing,*
> *For I feel my soul is singing*
> *To the music of the lathe upon its run . . .*

That was one of their politer songs.

In the end, Arthur's decision was partially made for him. With talk of conscription in the air, with men (and especially bachelors) being cajoled into military service under Lord Derby's Scheme, Arthur eventually felt that his time had come. The deciding factor was apparently trivial. A class of schoolgirls flocked self-consciously one dinner-time into the newly-organized canteen at Messrs Eli Wadsworth and Sons, to regale the workers with patriotic songs. They were collecting money, their teacher explained, in order to buy wool with which to knit socks and mittens for soldiers at the front. They even tried to sing the 'Marseillaise' in French. For all the sense it made, they

"EVERY MAN HIS CHANCE."

In conclusion, I want to drop for the moment my official position as Director-General, and to speak only as a man to men. This is the last organised effort on behalf of voluntary service. It is not the effort of an individual, it is the effort of the Parliamentary Recruiting Committee, a body of men representing all shades of politics, and including the Joint Labour Recruiting Committee, and all acting in thorough harmony.

It is an appeal to the people to recruit for the people, and it is an appeal which I hope will not be made in vain. It is the final appeal, and it is an appeal that gives every man his chance to give his services to his King and his country. The individual who stands back and does not come forward now, he is a man who declares he is not willing to help his country in the hour of stress. He is a man who would allow all the horrors of Belgium to go on in this country and yet stand back because he is afraid to take his part.

If at the end of our effort there is only that class of man standing out, do you think that the rest of the community will have much pity for him if he is forced to take his share?

45

needn't have bothered, but the intention was good. The following day, Arthur joined up.

*　　*　　*

Harry had joined the Army pale and under-nourished, but he filled out in training. With three solid meals every day, no opportunity for outside dissipations, and a fresh-air life of unremitting route marching, close and extended order drill, bayonet fighting and physical exercises, his Battalion grumbled and grew fit. For the first few months they moved around a good deal, but had little time to take in the sights. They became accustomed to bedding down wherever they were put, in barracks, tents, on straw palliasses on the floors of schools, in billets in private houses. For a while near York, they had an adjutant who delighted in spectacular textbook maneouvres, and who endlessly formed them in hollow squares to repel imaginary savage hordes. More appropriately, towards the end of the year, they were moved to the East Coast, where they strung barbed wire across the beaches (the tides regularly washed it away) and dug trenches along the cliffs, in which they sleepily 'stood to' an hour before dawn. It was there, on the misty morning when the Germans shelled Scarborough and Hartlepool, that Harry heard his first guns fired in anger, his company, shocked wide-awake, lining their parapet peering out across the grey murk of the booming sea. After that, with the rumour of enemy invasion, their entrenching and standing to achieved a distinctly realistic flavour.

The following spring, the battalion left for France, its four companies, complete with headquarters, signallers, quartermasters, transport and machine-gun section, slotted into three trains sliding down to Folkestone; the newspapers, as they crossed London, were full of casualty lists from a battle at Neuve Chapelle. They sailed the Channel by night, showing no lights, and marched into camp near Boulogne, whither they were pursued by a message from the Lord Mayor of the city in whose cathedral their regimental colours were laid up: 'You may rest fully assured that our good wishes for your welfare go with you, and we pray that, when the purposes of your mission are fulfilled, you will have a safe and speedy return to your homes.'

Next came weeks in which the battalion, shedding surplus equipment all the way, was moved back and forth behind the lines—a period summarized by a bespectacled Baptist Headquarters clerk who was always scribbling verses in an exercise book:

Right *More than 80 per cent of the workers in munitions factories were women. Here women's political emancipation was forged.*

47

We have a billet in a barn,
The cutest billet in the town.
In Rue de Four our billet is,
With straw as sweet as softest down.

Although at times the rain drips in,
And rats jump down on to your bed
From off the loft where turnips lie,
And lie and dye the raftings red.

Oh, Candas town, though only small,
Forever shall your name be writ
In this the book I call my life,
Until in heaven my soul shall sit!

As time passed and billets repeatedly changed, the straw grew dirtier and more sparse. Nights, cold and often wet, were a wretched alternation of chilled dozing and walking about in a futile bid to get warm.

They went eventually into a stretch of the front line known as the Duck's Bill by virtue of its shape, jutting out towards the enemy. The troops they relieved left them a row of shallow dug-outs infested with lice, and a cat called Wipers. Wipers, an unaffectionate lone tom covered with scarred bald patches, had no ears and a single bright green eye. His tireless occupation was catching the fat rats that thrived in the trenches. Everybody tried to make a fuss of Wipers, who was the best-fed soldier in the Duck's Bill. He was said to perform a similar service, receiving similar attentions, over in the German trenches.

By now, the war had ground to a stalemate in mud. The land around was flat and featureless, save for occasional ruins, and had recently been fought over, the brown violated earth pocked with craters and the air sickly with the smell of carrion. The days were hot. The dead lay everywhere, thrown down in abandoned attitudes, some swollen, others shrivelled inside their web of buckles, straps and pouches. Germans, French or British, they were indistinguishable, at one with the tumbled mud. Only the objects they had carried, their rifles, entrenching tools and mess-tins, kept their clear outlines.

In the Duck's Bill, Harry and his comrades learned, quickly and of necessity, the ways of trench warfare. They grew old within hours under the fire of shells and, even worse, trench mortars. They removed the badges and wires from their service caps, whose glint and parade-ground roundness would have offered too easy a mark for snipers. They became accustomed to shivering when it was cold, getting wet when it rained, sweating when it was warm. They felt dirty, and scratched themselves. They were simultaneously tense and

Right Home sweet home

numbed: to their stretched nerves were added lack of sleep and inadequate diet. They drank copiously of strong tea brewed with bad water and tasting of chloride of lime, and savoured a morning rum ration. They laboured to improve their trenches and dug-outs, were detailed for unceasing fatigues, bringing up sandbags, barbed wire, ammunition, rations (a company's bread occupied a big sack requiring four men to carry it). Their days began before dawn with 'stand to', followed by the artillery's 'morning hate'; ended with the dusk 'stand to' and another exchange of fire. Their nights were uncertain, as filled as their days with threat and activity. They crawled out into the horrors of No Man's Land, repairing their wire and observing the enemy, freezing whenever Verey lights illuminated their crazy landscape. The battalion occupied the Duck's Bill for ten days before being relieved and marching back into billets. They had lost eight killed and 21 wounded.

Private Harry Riley had been the seventh to die. Back at the Mission, somebody remembered his former casual attendance at Sunday School and reminded the Minister, who worked him into a sermon, together with his long-ago brother Stanley and the Boer War: quite properly, his theme was of 'heroic sacrifice'. In reality, however, there had seemed precious little of the heroic at the time. It had been during a brief, pointless artillery duel with the helpless Duck's Bill in the middle, when a shell (it might even have been one of

ours) had burst on the parapet directly above Harry, tearing him apart. At least, he was able to be buried on the spot, which was more than could be said for some of the poor bundles out in No Man's Land.

* * *

At the beginning of 1916, the Military Service Act came into force. 'Every male British subject' aged 18 to 41, who was unmarried or a widower without dependant children, was 'deemed to have been duly enlisted in His Majesty's regular forces for general service with the colours or in the reserve for the period of the war'. A number of opposing bodies sprang into action: the No-Conscription Fellowship, the Quakers ('We take the stand that it is criminal to take life and we are not prepared to take it'), the Trades Council and the Independent Labour Party ('This Act constitutes the cheapening of soldiers and the control of industry, and therefore a grave menace to the working classes and especially to organised workers').

They found the doors of public halls closed against them. Trying to organize public meetings, they were refused the hire of school-rooms and picture palaces. When the Society of Friends attempted an open discussion in their Meeting-House, both chairman and principal speaker were howled down within minutes, and the proceedings had to be abandoned. Two policemen in attendance remained seated throughout.

The local branch of the Independent Labour Party, holding a meeting in their own rooms, learned from the Quakers' experience and limited admission to ticket-holders. Ironically perhaps, their visiting speaker was a Liberal Member of Parliament, who thought that the introduction of conscription formed 'the turning-point in the history of liberty. As a nation', he pleaded, 'we could not abandon our most ancient and valuable traditions of individual liberty, and we could not accept the provisions of this Act without very serious moral consequences'. In the following debate, William Henry made an impassioned statement and got himself reported in the local newspaper: he felt it his 'duty' to oppose conscription. 'It would be', he said, 'an infringement of personal liberty, an infringement of industrial liberty, and an infringement of the liberty of conscience'.

Be that as it may, the Military Service Act had allowed for the exemption of men on important war work, those suffering from ill-health or whose conscription would cause serious hardship, or who held 'a conscientious objection to the undertaking of combatant service'. Local Tribunals were appointed to consider and interpret an understandably difficult rush of applications.

The Military Service Tribunal consisted of half-a-dozen well-meaning elderly gentlemen, an industrialist or two, a parson and a priest, an Alderman and a fierce individual known as the military representative. They were not greatly to be envied, sitting listening to poor farmers seeking exemption for indispensable sons, quarry-owners arguing to keep experienced engine-drivers, the Co-operative Society trying to clarify the position of its branch managers, small one-man businessmen whose careers were threatened with ruin. In a clumsy attempt to lighten the gravity of their decisions, and to put applicants at their ease, they tended to adopt a rather jocular manner, too often at the applicants' expense.

They were less humorous when it came to more complicated interviews with conscientious objectors. William Henry, called nervously before them, recited how he 'had a conscientious objection to war and militarism in any form. He had always been taught in his home life that war was wrong, and he believed, from the school of thought he was associated with, in the sanctity of human life'.

'What is the school of thought?' asked the Chairman.

'The Independent Labour Party.'

The gentlemen of the Tribunal exchanged glances among themselves. 'I do not think we can discuss that', observed the Chairman. 'I think you must base your arguments on your religious scruples.'

'As a matter of fact', William Henry pursued, 'I base them on the principles of the Independent Labour Party and the principles of Christ, and I take them to be on the same lines'.

The military representative leaned forward. 'Are you unwilling to take any part in the salvation of your country?' he demanded. 'What would you do if a Zeppelin were outside tonight, and you were in a position to destroy it and remove the peril? Would you do so or not?'

It was a startling hypothesis. 'I would not destroy the Zeppelin', said William Henry.

The Chairman sighed. 'I have nothing more to say', he shrugged; and they deferred their decision for further consideration. The military representative, however, could not resist a last word: 'You live in this country', he told William Henry, 'forgetting what people before you have done to secure freedom, yet you are not prepared to take any part in upholding freedom. I classify you as a coward'.

In the event, William Henry had a very difficult war. Parents of some of his pupils felt he was not fit to teach their children, and got up a petition against him: he was, they claimed, 'a perfect scandal'. The Tribunal, having considered his case, decided that his objection was of a political rather than a conscientious nature, the Central Appeal Tribunal were of the same opinion, and he was ordered to report for Army duty. He ignored the summons. He was arrested and handed over to a military escort. At the camp, he refused to put on a uniform. He was locked in a dirty guardroom where he had to sleep on the floor. He was offered an option of undertaking non-combatant duties, and turned it down. He was transferred to the civil authorities, brought before courts and subjected to such remarks as 'I am very sorry that you are an Englishman' and 'It is damnable that men are fighting to save such as you'. There were vague threats, never pursued, of a death penalty.

He passed through a series of gaols. He endured solitary confinement. In a cold medieval castle, he added his own terse statements to damp walls covered with pencilled drawings and religious texts: 'I was brought up from Leeds on Friday, August 11th, 1916, and put in this cell for refusing to become a soldier.' He spent four months in Wandsworth Prison and six weeks in Wormwood Scrubs. Drafted into outdoor labour camps, living in leaky tents which the Army had rejected, he struggled to mend roads and cut timber till his health broke down. Transferred to indoor work, permanently hungry, lodged precariously in workhouses (once in a lunatic asylum), he made brushes and baskets. He became especially proficient at stitching mailbags.

CHAPTER FIVE

THE SOMME

In the summer of 1916, the Allies planned a great offensive, in Picardy, on the Somme. With its 100,000 troops in the first assault, and another 400,000 in support, it was to make massive use of Kitchener's New Armies, still largely untapped, composed substantially of men who had grown up together, from the same towns, the same streets, the same schools, the same works.

So Corporal Arthur Illingworth found himself in an eager converging mass of units with names like the Grimsby Chums and the Belfast Young Citizens, the Newcastle Commercials, the Bantams, the Hull Sportsmen, Pals' battalions from Bradford and Accrington, Durham, Manchester, Liverpool, Leeds, arriving in a fresh green land of woods and fields of coloured flowers, of rolling chalk downs with the Germans dug solidly in on the higher ground.

In essence, the plan was dangerously simple. The British and French would greatly outnumber the enemy on this hitherto quiet section of the front. They would put down the biggest artillery bombardment the world had known, smashing the German trenches, cutting their wire and obliterating their defences. Then 100,000 infantry would advance, walking upright and heavily laden, meeting little opposition. Through the yawning gap they would make through the German front, would unleash the cavalry, pouring into a wide unscarred countryside where they could manoeuvre at will amongst a disorganized German rear. Stalemate would be broken. That was the plan.

So, for comparatively idyllic weeks in clean landscapes comfortably behind the lines, half a million soldiers rehearsed for the big offensive. Over and over, platoons practised with the bayonet: 'Advance, yell, charge and reform', instructed a Corps 'Notes on Training Infantry'. 'Every man to keep his eyes fixed on the man opposite him throughout.' Repeatedly, battalions impeccably advanced over tapes laid out to represent the German trench system, smugly capturing harsh Germanic signboards—Schwaben Redoubt, Leipzig Salient— symbolizing enemy strongpoints. It was a complex statistical exercise: each battalion advanced in waves at one-minute intervals, fighting platoons leading, followed by mopping-up, support and carrying platoons; there were five yards between each man, 100 yards between each wave, and their pace covered a steady 100 yards in two minutes. That, again, was the plan. 'When advancing to the attack', their Battle Orders advised, 'cheering and doubling should not be allowed. The former advertises the fact that troops are attacking and the latter is too great an effort to men carrying heavy weights'.

Fatigues continued on a spectacular scale. Mighty dumps of ammunition, food and fodder accumulated behind the front. A network of assembly trenches was scooped laboriously out of the earth, the white vulnerable chalk carried away sack by sack out of sight of the watchful enemy. Issued with the new, bowl-shaped steel helmets, men tested their usefulness by hitting one another playfully over the heads with spade-handles. Towards the end of June, the bombardment opened (a gun to every 17 yards of front), the night sky ablaze and the days filled with earth-shaking thunder.

Letters home were strictly censored, and it was forbidden to keep diaries lest they fall into enemy hands and betray intentions. Yet Arthur, made for once in his life curiously aware of the shaping of history, contrived each day to pencil a few words in a tiny pocket-book. He had invented a code of which he was quite proud (but which would not, alas, have placed undue difficulty in the path of German intelligence), basically a question of transferring the first letter of each word to the back and adding a superfluous letter. 'Rigadebe hurchco ervicest', he gravely recorded. 'Etso ffof not outerr archmo utbe erewt ismissedd orfg ewislm ungg racticeps' (Brigade church service. Set off on route march but were dismissed for Lewis gun practice).

Steadily, his daily entries grew more urgent (orkingwo nit eserverr inell' . . . 'eepeningdo upportst renchtt' — working in reserve line . . . deepening support trench), culminating in a spate of 'xtraes eavyho ombardmentbo' and 'eavyho hellingso' and 'hizzwu angsbo' (extra heavy bombardment, heavy shelling, whizz-bangs).

It was difficult not to feel fearfully impressed, marching up at last to the front. Each soldier bristled weightily with packs and webbing, waterproof sheet, gas-mask, 220 rounds of ammunition, two Mills bombs, water-bottle, extra rations, three empty sandbags, Lee-Enfield rifle and bayonet — additionally, Arthur carried a pick stuck down his back behind his pack. Yet their boots tramped cheerfully along the straight roads, for they had been told their attack could not fail ('You will find the Germans all dead, not even a rat will have survived', a speech-making Brigadier-General had assured them), and here and there man sang. Over the crazy cobbles of the red-brick, ruined town of Albert they marched, under the Madonna and Child hanging (strengthened with cable) out of the shelled Basilica tower. A few threadbare civilians came silently out of cellars to watch them pass.

The nearer they marched to the sound of the guns, with their row of observation balloons marking the front, the more congested grew the movement of men, mules, horses, limbers, waggons, lorries. The land became one vast khaki maelstrom lightly coated with chalk-dust. They approached tidy new dumps from which, platoon by platoon, were added yet more burdens in the shape of mallets, duck-boards,

Right Under severe fire and hampered by their own wire men go into the attack. On the far right one goes down.

rolls of wire. They saw acres of waiting cavalry, British troopers with sabres, turbanned Indians whose lances fluttered with bright pretty pennants. They passed field-kitchens, farriers, military policemen, latrines, gas containers, mobile lofts for carrier-pigeons, signallers unravelling cables and testing field-telephones, huge mounds of empty shell-cases, and their own artillery with methodical bare-armed gunners, dug into pits, shielded by earthworks, draped with camouflage matting. With varied emotions they noted empty barbed-wire prisoner-of-war pens confidently ready for their expected enemy; big tented Casualty Clearing Stations, white and as yet unbloodied; and long waiting mass graves.

Presently it began to rain, and they slowly ground to a halt. Orders came: the offensive was to be postponed for 48 hours, in the hope of better weather. In the meantime, the Army lapsed into a miserable limbo. Arthur squatted under his waterproof in a shallow hole in the side of an embankment, relished an issue of bully beef stew, listened to the bombardment. There was a lull each night to enable patrols to go out and examine the German defences, and some disturbing stories were filtering back from the trenches: No Man's Land was littered with unexploded British shells . . . the enemy wire remained largely uncut . . . the Germans—after days under intensive fire—had actually been heard in their dug-outs, singing!

They moved forward again on the night of 30 June, and this time there would be no more delays. Men filed quietly through the darkness, following tapes towards their assembly trenches, crowding together in a soaking dew. Arthur was in position just before dawn (momentarily he heard a lark going up), but this was to be no sudden half-light attack, and hours of further waiting lay ahead. He watched

the summer's day open beautifully with a clear blue sky and the mist rising from the hollows. At this point No Man's Land presented a gently sloping meadowland, still recognisably green and sprinkled with poppies and wild flowers. There was nothing to do except wait and hope breakfast would get through—it didn't, although the rum ration miraculously did, but a teetotal captain poured it all down a hole. This did not create an auspicious stomach for battle.

At 6.25 am began a final concentrated bombardment of the German defences, and this at least was invigorating. Soldiers could not resist cheering, even feeling an awed pity for the mortals at the heart of that continuous thunder of leaping earth and stone. Surely their optimistic Generals must have been right, surely nothing could have withstood the past week of pounding artillery! But the British bombardment drew a return German fire which, along that waiting, congested front, could not fail to find targets; and men, who had drilled and trained and rehearsed for months—some for nearly two years—died or were mutilated without firing a shot or advancing a pace towards their enemy.

Arthur's platoon—one of his battalion's rear carrying waves—cowered amongst its shuddering impedimenta of stakes and boards and rolled wire, pressed along its crumbling trench-walls as shrapnel and debris hurtled overhead. Just before zero, a mine was blown nearby, sending skywards a dark gigantic pillar of disintegrating earth, the shock running among them so violently that a Lance-Corporal, who had been bracing himself against the parapet, fell writhing with a fractured leg.

At 7.30 am, still true to the plan, the barrage suddenly lifted from the enemy front, pausing before moving on to its next targets, and there was a moment of silence. Again, bird-song was audible. Long slender bayonets had been fixed. Where the trenches lay deepest, ladders stood in position against the parapets, beneath which, heads instinctively bowed, soldiers queued Officers and Sergeant-Majors ostentatiously consulted their watches.

Then whistles shrilled all along the British line, and steel-helmeted platoons poured up endlessly out of the ground: the Hull Tradesmen, the Derry Volunteers, the Glasgow Tramways, Pals' battalions from Salford and Barnsley.... Long rows of khaki infantry looked nervously to left and right, checking their intervals, stepped delicately through their own wire and, their rifles held stiffly before them, began their deliberate, practised walk across No Man's Land. Their officers strode conspicuously among them, some waving sticks. But the enemy artillery found them; machine-guns rattled from the pulverized higher ground (for the Germans had not all been killed, by any means); and row after row the slow khaki soldiers fell. More followed them, wave after wave, to topple in their turn amongst the shell-holes. Dimly, through drifting smoke and exploding earth, a few distant figures could be glimpsed, held up at the uncut enemy wire until, bunching together at occasional gaps, they too went down in heaps.

Years later, when history books had been written, Arthur would read about this morning. He would learn of 20,000 killed in a single day, of another 40,000 wounded, of rare desperate footholds in the German line, and of overall failure (the cavalry never did break through). But for the present, his mind could not grasp the enormity of these plodding rows of men disappearing, one after another, into the empty dissolving landscape.

Nor could one look on detached, for there was no safety anywhere: enemy fire was falling heavily now on the British positions, as carrying platoons struggled out of their trenches. Next to Arthur, two privates were clambering up the parapet with, between them, a roll of barbed wire wrapped round a stake. Slinging his rifle, he lent them a hand. From one of the privates suddenly issued a sound as of a loud, sodden smack, and he was gone, just his helmet spinning on its rim on a sandbag; his end of the stake fell back into the trench. Arthur hurried to pick it up. There was blood everywhere, on the wire and on the stake, and it transferred liberally to his hands, his trousers, his tunic. The remaining private was very young and very thin and very frightened, and all the while he sobbed and muttered a monotonous stream of obscenities. Between them, they got the wire up again out of the trench. Then the thin young private unexpectedly dropped his end of the stake, his obscenities rising to a screamed urgency, and began to tear off his straps and buckles; he half jumped, half fell back into the trench and stumbled lop-sidedly away, his whole body hunched over a new centre of gravity about his red right hip. Arthur had no option but to let go his end, too. The rolled wire lay for a moment on top of the parapet, then slowly turned over and fell back into the bottom of the trench. Arthur left it and started after his platoon.

There was an unreal, nightmarish quality about the experience of battle, which shrank to his own immediate impressions, and they were blurred. The noise—whining and crashing and clattering— was deafening, the air prickly with fumes and smoke, alive with unseen missiles, the earth jumping unpredictably in machine-gunned spurts and shelled eruptions. Aware of a haunting undercurrent of groans, Arthur—without really looking—stepped around fallen men, some still, others crawling and moving (orders were not to stop to help wounded). But he did not advance far for, his left leg felt suddenly numb, he sprawled headlong. He got up, but his leg failed him and he fell down again. There was more blood, and he sickly realised that it wasn't all the private's off the stake and rolled wire—his puttee trailed behind, and his trouser-leg hung ragged. Investigating, he caught a glimpse of his own grey shin-bone with his bright red blood pulsing around it; and at the same time, a realisation of pain flooded over him. Arthur vomited into his lap and momentarily blacked out, slipping over the slimy edge of a shell-hole.

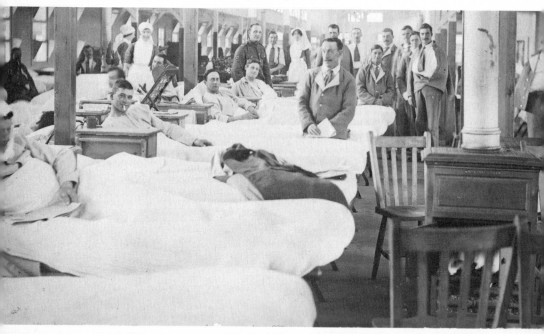

CHAPTER SIX

THE HOME FRONT

What Arthur had thus expensively acquired was one of the Blighty wounds much envied by the older hands. He was luckier than many, too, in being picked up by stretcher-bearers fairly quickly. They applied a field dressing to his leg and got him back into the trenches he had so recently left, now battered and littered with dead. He would retain only a sketchy impression of his homeward journey.

The harrassed Medical Officer at the battalion first-aid post simply passed him back to the Dressing Station, through crowded communication trenches, caught up in a rearward ebb of wounded, his stretcher bumping and banging, tilted now this way, now that. At the Dressing Station they improved somewhat on his bandaging, gave him morphia and loaded him into a motor ambulance. Semi-conscious (one of the other men in the ambulance died during the ride), he was aware, through the jolting back flaps, of a slowly-overtaken procession of walking wounded, their dishevelled khaki lividly enlivened with red blood and white bandages. At the Casualty Clearing Station he was laid on straw in a field filled with soiled wounded, the arrangements for their further evacuation having, it seemed, temporarily broken down under the strain of their unanticipated numbers. At some point he was lifted into a tent, examined and lifted out again. He lay on his back, the sun shining annoyingly into his eyes. Orderlies were stepping constantly among the waiting bodies, and one noticed his distress and put a newspaper over his face. Night came down.

Later he became aware of lying, gently swaying, in an ambulance train—aware, too, of dull discomfort whenever the train broke its steady rhythm. He was still wearing most of his uniform, stiff with dried mud, and a medical card hung round his neck. A purple cross on his forehead indicated that he had been given morphia. But again Arthur had been lucky: the evacuation of wounded was flowing comparatively smoothly now, and he dozed and woke alternately on and off the hospital ship. 'Andedlm tap overdo', he would much later write in his pocket-book, loth to abandon his code. Another night, and another ambulance train was taking him northwards from Dover.

The train came to a halt at four o'clock in the morning, as dawn was breaking with a chorus of birds. A small squad of the Royal Army Medical Corps waited on the railway station with a crowd of local Voluntary Aid Men and the St John Ambulance Brigade. Some of them had been up most of the night, preparing. The train carried 120 stretcher cases who, when lifted out and laid side by side, stretched from one end of the platform to the other. The unloading was accomplished in a strangely hushed atmosphere. At the station entrance, a cluster of officers (they were civilian doctors given military rank for the duration) held a brief muted consultation over each stretcher set down in turn before them; and beyond, an elderly couple gave a handful of cigarettes to every conscious wounded man. Outside in the station yard, a motley collection of vehicles waited, took in wounded, drove away and returned empty for more—motor ambulances, provided by public subscription and embellished with the civic coats-of-arms of neighbouring towns; touring cars for the walking cases, some converted to take stretchers; and several vans, still proclaiming along their sides: Stockbridge Finishing Company. The summer's day was fully astir by the time the wounded from the far end of the platform were in hospital.

The War Hospital had, until recently, specialized in civilian fever treatment, and stood outside the town at the foot of the moors. The garden areas between its stone buildings had been largely taken over by new wards of creosoted wood and asbestos sheeting. Some of these would hold upwards of 200 men, being tightly filled with beds, though spaces at regular intervals were occupied by stoves and by tables which a ladies' visiting committee kept colourful with vases of flowers. The patients had come together from all parts of Great Britain, and from the Empire.

As a means of sustaining morale, the War Hospital published its own magazine, compiled by and for patients and staff; wherein the Administrator outlined his functions, a staff nurse and a young probationer described their duties, and a private of the Highland Light Infantry wrote weightily on 'The Patriotic Spirit in Hospital'. Most of the remaining pages comprised jokes and facetious verses:

> *When you to come to the end of a perfect day,*
> *And you lie all alone in your bed,*
> *Your thoughts are by no means clear and gay*
> *For the Major to you has said—*
> *'No food, but some castor-oil you'll take,*
> *And then towards ten of the clock,*
> *The nose-cap over your mouth shall make*
> *Your brain have an awful shock' . . .*

The War Hospital's population changed constantly but, this summer of 1916, was in process of massively swelling, with ambulance trains arriving frequently. These occasions were preceded by determined activity in the wards. All the scattered empty beds were moved together, some of the convalescents helping. Supplies of fresh sheets, blue suits, flannel shirts, slippers and towels were drawn from the stores, charts and diet-cards pinned to boards above beds 'all neatly

Right 'Memories': a page from a war hospital magazine.

made', as the staff nurse expressed it, 'with the clothes rolled back, to be in perfect readiness'. This same staff nurse, describing the arrival of those convoys of motor ambulances, touring cars and vans of the Stockbridge Finishing Company, had noted how the faces of the new wounded looked 'happy and contented, proclaiming the fact that their dreams have really come true and "Blighty" has become a reality'.

The convalescent wounded wore blue hospital suits, sometimes with the trousers tucked mightily up at the ankles, being too long. With their khaki caps—or glengarries or slouch hats—perched atop bandages, with empty sleeves or arms in slings, with walking-sticks or crutches, they got about the wards and grounds, posed for comradely photographs. Whenever one of the patients died, as was frequently the case, the coffin would be followed to its rest by a serious, hobbling blue column.

('The fortitude with which the wounded bear their sufferings is a national characteristic', the Highland Light Infantry private had recorded. 'The optimistic cheerfulness pervading the wards is infectious, and allows scant opportunity for morbid reflection. It manifests itself in good-humoured banter, song and story, indicating the reaction of spirits previously oppressed by the fatigues and anxieties of war.')

A. Henley. '17.

The wards were visited, daytime and evening, by many well-meaning townsfolk. Craftsmen and talented ladies taught woodcarving and crotcheting, and soldiers developed quite a craze for embroidering their regimental badges. Concert parties entertained, comics and singers came from theatres as far afield as Leeds and Manchester. Two nights each week, films lent by one or another of the town's picture houses whirred and flickered: 'The Price of her Silence' (a romantic drama of the unselfish devotion of a strong-willed girl for her weak and younger sister) . . . 'The Game of Life' (depicting in no half-measures the temptations of a pretty girl) . . . 'The Survivor' (full of exciting and thrilling incidents in the terrific struggle between the Italians and the Austrians) . . . But most men's favourite was Charlie Chaplin. In the middle of the Hospital buildings stood a recreation room, to which solid citizens had donated billiard-tables; often these were moved aside to make way for whist drives. There was also a large wooden chapel, put together by superhuman efforts on the part of the Chaplain: attendances, however, were not very encouraging.

('Wounded soldier, minus one leg, reclining on bed, with a lady visitor approaching him', ran one of the magazine jokes.

'Lady Visitor, to soldier: "Well, my good man, I am sorry to see you have lost a leg."

'Soldier: "Yes, madam, but I wish it had been the other one, as that is the one with the rheumatics in it." ')

Along the lower end of the War Hospital went the canal, whereon convalescents were advised to row in boats borrowed specially from the seaside; a sporting gentleman had brought his motor launch all the way from the Lake District to place at the disposal of the less active. Sometimes, soldiers were invited into neighbouring schools for tea and concerts, and occasionally a fortunate few were treated to motor rides. The School of Art had started bookbinding classes which, it was felt, might help provide a future source of livelihood for those permanently disabled.

*   *   *

Eventually discharged, with a permanent limp, as unfit for further military service, Arthur returned to a civilian world very different from the one he had left. Life now in every aspect had taken on a grey cast. Small newspaper print of the personal columns carried appeals: 'Lance-Corporal W. Edwards, 8th Yorks. and Lancs., missing since July 1st. Any information gladly received by his parents, Mr and Mrs J. Edwards, Emerald Street.' Every week, the local paper was publishing lists of killed, wounded, missing and prisoners. 'Heroes of the Great Advance', the headlines had reiterated the previous summer (Great Advance?—Arthur remembered his meagre patch of chalky mud); now they simply said: 'Fallen in the War'.

Right *This advertisement seems ironic in comparison to the three preceding photographs.*

Week after week, an adjoining column ran an advertisement showing a drawing of a soldier wearing a padded vest. 'Ensure your Loved One's Safety', cajoled its legend, 'by immediately soliciting an order for a "Chemico" Fabric Body Shield, which has proved to be a real life-saver.' The padded vest was available in various sizes, single or double thickness, with optional abdominal attachment, and apparently (there were testimonials to prove the point) it had withstood numerous tests, 'including Bayonet Thrusts, Service Revolvers, Bullets, and Flying Shrapnel'. Arthur remained unconvinced.

Now, there were noticeably few fit youngish men about. Conscription was casting its net ever more widely, and raw boys were being called up, with middle-aged men who had already lost sons. A vociferous public opinion was raising the search for reluctant recruits to the tempo of a witch-hunt. Words had been coined to fit the occasion. There were 'comb-outs' of workers in exempted occupations, 'round-ups' of those deemed to be 'shirkers'. The authorities were even reduced to raiding common lodging-houses and sweeping up any sorry serviceable flotsam they found there.

Everywhere, in industries and offices and on the land, women were doing men's jobs. Briskly, in smart dark uniforms, they collected tram-fares, and the Corporation Tramways had recently experimented with lady drivers. Unfortunately, the worst conditions had prevailed: street lighting was reduced, tracks and stock deteriorated (some trams had been purchased from Austria shortly before the war, so spare parts were unobtainable!), and the winter had been bleak and sleety. For once, the Tramways Manager and the Tramway and Vehicle Workers' Union (and emphatically Arthur's father) had been in agreement: women were 'not fitted temperamentally or physically for driving'. There had consequently been some discussion as to the alternative of employing disabled men; again with a unanimous conclusion that 'only men with both hands, both legs and both feet should be entrusted with the driving of trams as at present designed'.

There was unrest on all sides. Wages had risen, but so had prices and everybody felt unsettled. Messrs Eli Wadsworth and Sons, where Arthur had been gratefully received back into his old job, had difficulty keeping their spinners because they could earn more at the munitions works. All the Co-operative Society's shops shut for several days because women who had filled men's places wanted putting on the men's wage scale; and in any case the remaining men were demanding higher wages. So were carters, who struck. When the question of women tram drivers had been mooted, the men had threatened to strike; and when the men were given a bonus, the conductresses went on strike till they got one too. Some of the munitions girls talked of similar action, but thought better of it in face of the displeasure of a Munitions Tribunal.

Munitions work was ageing Arthur's sister Connie, but she stuck to it with weary determination, snatching time with her little girl and waiting for brief pencilled cards from her soldier-husband. Now she wore trousers to match her brown overall. She had volunteered for the factory's recent shell-filling extension, and her skin and hair—even her eyebrows—had turned yellow from the TNT she handled. She worked in a strange atmosphere of rumour and secrecy: there were explosions at Leeds, but the censors hushed them up. When, not many miles away, a picric acid works had disastrously blown up, the Ministry of Munitions authorized only a short statement to the press. Loss of life, they reassured, had proved 'not so serious as at first seemed probable' (actually, 39 had been killed, and 'one man still unaccounted for'); whilst 'the patriotic energy immediately displayed by other manufacturers in the country will prevent the diminution of the total production'.

Facts had grown difficult to assess. You heard gossip and rumour,

Below The Times *reports the German spring offensive of 1918.*

Right *Suspension of the drink traffic!*

THE TIMES, SATURDAY, MARCH 23, 1918.

SECOND DAY OF BATTLE.

ENEMY ADVANCE AT GREAT PRICE.

GALLANT BRITISH DIVISIONS.

The following telegraphic dispatches were received from General Headquarters in France yesterday :—

11.47 A.M.—Fighting continued till a late hour last night on the whole front between the River Oise and the River Sensée. Our troops continued to hold the enemy in their battle positions.

During the enemy's attacks yesterday his massed infantry offered remarkable targets to our rifles, machine-guns, and artillery, of which full advantage was taken by our troops. All reports testify to the exceedingly heavy losses suffered by the enemy.

No serious attack has yet developed this morning, but heavy fighting is still to be expected.

altitude, in which 16 hostile machines were brought down and six were driven down out of control. A hostile balloon was destroyed by one of our pilots, and one of the enemy's low-flying aeroplanes was shot down in our lines by our infantry. Three of our machines are missing.

During the night our night-flying squadrons in the southern area of the front were unable to leave the ground owing to the mist.

In the northern area, where the weather was clear, our aeroplanes dropped three and a half tons of bombs on the dockyards at Bruges and three and a half tons on rest billets north-west of Tournai. All our machines returned.

LARGE ENEMY CLAIMS.

FIRST LINES "EVERYWHERE CAPTURED."

GERMAN official report, March 22 :—

FRONTS OF CROWN PRINCE RUPPRECHT AND THE GERMAN CROWN PRINCE.—Ostend has been bombarded from the sea.

In Belgian and French Flanders a strong artillery duel continued. Reconnoitring detachments penetrated on many occasions into the enemy lines.

From south-east of Arras as far as La Fère we attacked the English positions. After powerful fire by our artillery and mine-throwers our infantry stormed in broad sectors, and

GREAT BRITISH DEFENCE.

HEROIC FIGHTING AGAINST ODDS.

STORY OF THE ATTACK.

(From Our Special Correspondent.)

WAR CORRESPONDENTS' HEADQUARTERS, MARCH 22.

The great battle has begun.

After a winter of intense preparation and long suspense, the Germans yesterday launched the blow which, they hope, will yield them that final victory in the West which is to give them the triumphant peace the people have been promised.

The weight with which the blow is being delivered may be judged from the fact that already nearly 40 German divisions, including four divisions of the Guard, have been identified as in action on the British front. On one section of the front no fewer than 17 German divisions were in the course of one day thrown against five British divisions; almost, indeed, against four

se has ttle in larger the ment. ecause domi- ularly have ; they Aus- n un- garian ng in a time ar. On a sheer though re not anders. erthe- Allied ve no n they r half ow we longer. e con- d, un- st, and the

hints and whispers, yet you shuffled the newspaper pages in vain. Occasionally you heard noises and saw lights in the sky at night, but you were never told they were British airships so you feared German Zeppelins. If the Germans advanced—as, early in 1918, they did, spectacularly—the headlines praised our Splendid Resistance and Brilliant Counter-Attacks: we were always Heroically Fighting Against Tremendous Odds, Wiping Out Enemy Masses and Firmly Holding Our Withdrawn Lines. By 1917, you were fairly sure there had been food riots not too far away, but the papers never mentioned them.

Lesser individual freedoms were vanishing under the guise of helping the war effort. Take Regulation 7 of the Liquor Control Order: Arthur, neither teetotal nor regular drinker, recalled with some affection the stalwarts of the pre-war Temperance Society—they were fighting, at its extreme, a real social evil, and they ran a showmanlike programme of concerts, sing-songs and sermons, determinedly handing out their pamphlets and organizing their Bands of Hope. But the 'No-Treating Order' was cold and savage. Arthur witnessed Regulation 7 in operation on his second evening as a civilian, sitting in the Boltmakers' Arms. A man came in with three women and said, 'Now, lasses, what are you going to have?' and, as he bought their drinks, two plainclothes constables slipped out to return a minute later with their Inspector. The customer, the three women, the barman and the publican were all heavily fined. 'There

STRENGTH OF BRITAIN MOVEMENT.

SUSPENSION OF THE DRINK TRAFFIC

DURING WAR AND DEMOBILISATION.

GREAT MASS MEETING

MUNICIPAL HALL, KEIGHLEY, JUNE 11TH, 1917.

— OFFICERS. —

| Chairman:
MR. EUSTACE H. ILLINGWORTH.

Hon. Treasurer:
MR. EUSTACE H. ILLINGWORTH. | Hon. Financial Secretary
MRS. GROVES,
CASTLE VILLA, KEIGHLEY. | Hon. Joint Secretaries:
MR. H. FIRTH,
WINDYGARTH, KEIGHLEY.

MR. W. J. JOHNS,
HAWTHORN HOUSE, OAKWORTH. |

HAWTHORN HOUSE,
OAKWORTH, nr. KEIGHLEY.

Dear Sir, or Madam,

The Executive Committee organising the above Demonstration, feeling that you will be willing to support their effort, have pleasure in acquainting you with the Resolution which will be spoken to and submitted to the Meeting :—

"That, in order to avert the danger of famine, with the consequent risk of a premature and disastrous peace, this meeting calls upon the Government to wholly suspend the manufacture and sale of alcohol during the war and the period of demobilisation, and thus immediately save the food of several millions of persons. That a copy of this Resolution be sent to His Majesty's Ministers."

From the foregoing it will be seen that the Resolution embodies a strictly emergency proposal, which ought to command the support of all citizens anxious to see the country emerge successfully from this terrible conflict.

In the endeavour to make the Meeting fully representative of all shades of thought and activity in the Keighley district, a cordial invitation is extended to you to support the platform. In the case of a favourable reply, a numbered seat will be reserved for your convenience.

An early reply will be esteemed.

Yours faithfully,

HENRY FIRTH } Joint Hon.
W. J. JOHNS } Secretaries.

were', thundered the prosecuting solicitor, in shocked tones, 'forty-seven women in the public-house at the time!'

Even more extreme, a Strength of Britain Movement was advocating the complete suspension of what it called 'the drink traffic' for the duration of the war!

A multitude of organizations was raising money for a myriad worthy causes—indeed, for all its drabness, life had never been busier. There were garden fetes and Hospital Sings (thousands of voices hymn-singing in the open air in aid of the wounded), Grand Patriotic Balls and concerts on behalf of the Mayoress's Fund for Soldiers' Winter Comforts. Novelty football and cricket matches—the Royal Horse Artillery versus a Team of Munition Workers; the Police versus the Special Police. Flag days for the British Red Cross, for the French Relief Fund, the Serbian Relief Fund, for an Anglo-Russian Hospital Fund doomed to extinction in 1917.

Make your cheques out; get your cash out;
Give with all your might and main
That these valiant Russian soldiers
May be nursed to health again.

At earlier wartime Christmases, the National Committee for Relief in Belgium had hit on an idea: 'Please pass this envelope round your dinner table on Christmas Day and help to feed 3,000,000 Belgians in Belgium, who are destitute, and whom the Germans refuse to feed.' Now, a Syria and Palestine Relief Fund was piling on its own horrors: 'Famine in the Holy Land! Syria and Palestine sharing the fate of Armenia! 3,500,000 destitute and dying! Men, women and children are falling dead in the streets every day! Their only crime is that they sympathize with the British and their Allies!'

There was a Prisoners of War Brotherhood Fund, and a British Society for Relief of Belgian Wounded Soldiers, and a YMCA Huts Fund (the latter greatly helped by an indefatigable concert party, The Vaudevilles) . . . There was a Submarine War Investment Week which brought an exhibition aeroplane—surrounded by collecting-boxes—into the town; and an Aeroplanes Effort which invited people 'to invest £10 each in War Bonds or War Savings Certificates' . . . And not quite all the activity was pulling in the same direction. 'Public Meeting!' cried a cantankerous poster in 1917, '*You* are cordially asked to come and hear a *true* statement of what we are fighting for.'

Nearer and nearer, hunger stalked. Queues waited for hours outside grocery stores, and a shop opened for the sale of horse-meat. The workhouse inmates were slipped unobtrusively on to a trial diet of porridge and pease pudding which, after a fortnight, was proved to be inadequate. On 2 May 1917, the King issued a Proclamation

Right Great War charity stickers.

66

exhorting heads of households to reduce the consumption of bread, and the population was encouraged to wear purple ribbons as a token of frugality. Circulars from the Ministry of Food took on a note of urgency: 'We must all eat less food; especially we must all eat less bread, and none of it must be wasted. The enemy is trying to take away our daily bread. He is sinking our wheat ships. If he succeeds in starving us, our soldiers will have died in vain.'

Food—the obtaining of food and the saving of food—became an obsession. Flower-beds in the public parks were replaced with potatoes, cauliflowers and cabbages, and part of the golf links went under oats. New ground was broken for allotments, and the Trade and Grammar School boys dug up their football field. Schoolchildren were treated to little ersatz loaves made out of oatmeal, pearl barley, rice, maize; taken outdoors for lessons on wild edible greenstuffs; taught to chorus propaganda songs like 'Wear the Purple Ribbon' and 'Each Loaf Saved Drives a Big, Long Nail'. Housewives attending lectures and cookery demonstrations, were shown how to make lentil roast, barley scones, war jam, and date pudding without using flour. A prominent shop-window, taken over for the duration by the local Food Control Committee, exhibited an ideal one day's rations for one

Below *Queueing for margarine, 1917.*   Right *A ration poster.*

Waste not
Want not!

SAVE
THE
NATION'S
BREAD

NATIONAL 4lb EACH
RATION PER WEEK

(2566). Wt. P99/941. 1,000,000. 4/17. P.P.Ltd. Est. No. 1128. **F.C.—4.**

Mr. Slice o'Bread.

"I am a Slice of Bread.

I measure three inches by two-and-a-half, and my thickness is half-an-inch.

My weight is exactly an ounce.

I am wasted once a day by 48,000,000 people of Britain.

I am 'the bit left over'; the slice eaten absent-mindedly when really I wasn't needed; I am the waste crust.

If you collected me and my companions for a whole week you would find that we amounted to 9,380 tons of good bread—**WASTED!**

Two Shiploads of Good Bread!

Almost as much—striking an average—as twenty German Submarines could sink—even if they had good luck.

When you throw me away or waste me you are adding twenty submarines to the German Navy."

National War Savings Committee, Salisbury Square, E.C. 4.

person—six small dusty sausages, half a loaf, and half a saucer of sugar. Eventually, accompanied by a bureaucratic paraphernalia of margarine cards, sugar tickets and meat cards, rationing was introduced ('When purchasing meat you MUST take with you your Butter Card. The butcher will then record, in red, your purchase for any one week'), but still the queues waited and shopkeepers grew more harrassed.

Now and again, morale was boosted. One beautiful summer's day in 1918, the Royal train came panting busily along the valley, slowing down near a bunch of nurses and a rank of wounded soldiers saluting in the fields alongside the tracks. The King and Queen spent a carefully scheduled 55 minutes viewing the town's contribution to the war effort. The King was a rather tired-looking gentleman with a beard and impeccable military uniform (complete with spurs), the

Queen a stately, gracious lady, and they somehow managed to make their few precise minutes appear leisured and informal. At a textile mill they chatted to the oldest workers (eight men with 427 years' service between them); at the shell factory, the munitions girls struck up a spontaneous 'God Save the King' and crowds joined in; and at the Town Hall, stiff with local dignitories, they singled out a poor widow woman who had lost three of her four sons, the fourth at that moment lying seriously wounded in France.

But the Armistice, when at last it came, was an anticlimax. That autumn of 1918 brought an influenza epidemic which, the world over, killed an estimated ten million. At home, it simply meant that people complained of sore throats and a sudden rise in temperature, taking to their beds where—weakened perhaps in body and spirit by the war years—many developed complications and died. Whole industries, their workers absent, slowed down. Schools closed for a fortnight; picture houses and concerts were advised not to admit children. By early November, so many were dying that the Cemetery couldn't cope, and waterworks navvies were called in to help dig graves, at night by the light of lanterns. Early one morning, outside the railway station, Arthur saw a high stack of shiny mass-produced coffins, which shocked him as profoundly as the Somme had done.

Since the spring, when her husband had gone missing and was since presumed dead, Arthur's sister Connie had returned to live with her parents. The day before the schools closed, her little girl came home out of sorts; the next day she was gravely ill; and the day after that she died. The following week, the whole family went down together— Arthur's mother made strenuous efforts to keep going, but had to give in. There seemed little the overworked doctor could do, although he scandalized clean Mrs Illingworth by throwing all their bed-hangings down the stairs ('germ-ridden fol-di-rols', he called them). So they all lay in bed, whilst Mrs Illingworth's equally energetic sister walked twice a day from the other side of town, to minister to their more pressing needs and feed the hens on Arthur's father's allotment. In due course they recovered, except poor Connie, whose influenza turned to pneumonia, and she died.

On 11 November, not yet fit for work, Arthur limped weakly out. All the factories, some of the shops, even the trams had stopped by early afternoon. It was a bright day, more like spring than autumn, and the streets were thronged with people walking soberly about. Quietly, flags were appearing, most of the children had them in readiness (for the Armistice had been rumoured for weeks), whilst the Parish Church bells rang sporadic peals. Cruelly, for months yet, the newspapers continued to publish dwindling lists of local casualties.

Above right Preparation for the great Peace Celebrations—a splendid gaiety in a drab street.

Below right . . . and a factory.

The year closed with a General Election. For the first time, in recognition of their war work, women aged 30 and over were entitled to vote. ('How long', demanded a heckler at an election meeting, 'are ladies who are under 30 likely to wait before they get the vote?' 'That depends', suavely replied the speaker, to laughter, 'how much under 30 they are at the present time'.) Arthur's mother, pale and saddened, was determined to exercise her new right. Knowing nothing of politics, she ignored the confident young Labour candidate and an unknown Coalition Unionist, and, with a majority of her mature townswomen, voted safely, familiarly Liberal.

CHAPTER SEVEN

THE GERMAN FIELD GUN

During February and March of the following year, influenza returned to strike, amongst other places, at The Raikes. Some miles up the valley, where the factories ended and the gentler green Dale began, The Raikes had comprised, until a couple of years ago, a number of large fields; more recently occupied by an internment camp for German officer prisoners-of-war. Little was seen or heard of the Germans. Just once a newspaper editor had permitted them a mention in his columns. 'They include some with distinguished careers', he had written. 'One is a submarine commander whose exploits include the sinking of a hospital ship, while another is a flying-officer for whom it is claimed that he has dropped more bombs on London than any other man.'

Now for three months the war had been over, but the Germans, hundreds of them, still lived behind barbed wire, half-heartedly teaching themselves languages and mathematics in their cramped wooden hutments, the spaces between having acquired a dull and trodden look; and their bored guards still mounted and dismounted at strict intervals, killing their off-duty hours in the nearest public houses. The German officers were attended by German orderlies, and contrived to keep themselves as presentable as circumstances would allow. They did not get much fresh air, and the influenza which attacked The Raikes was, perhaps in consequence, especially virulent, with pneumonic complications.

So, three and four months after the war had ended, many of these German officers died, the pilots and the submarine commanders, and their orderlies died with them. Every day for a fortnight, they were buried in fours and fives and half-dozens, in a corner set apart at the Cemetery, already speckled with British graves from the War Hospital. Their coffins would drive slowly along the road in the back of a lorry, a solemn, upright and slightly shabby delegation of German officers marching silently behind. At the Cemetery, beyond the long heaped clay of the open grave, a khaki firing party would be waiting, leaning on the butts of their reversed rifles. A knot of the curious would be gathered there too (these tended to diminish after the first few days, as the novelty wore off), and a clergyman—sometimes several clergymen if more than one denomination was involved. Usually, during the service, a German officer would take a pace forward and say a prayer. The spectacular moment would arrive when, the coffins having been lowered into the earth, the firing party discharged three volleys into the air.

Even before the epidemic had quite run its course, surviving officers were, with typical efficiency, collecting funds and organizing their talents towards a monument to their dead. Indeed, the resultant German memorial (understandably fairly modest, in brick) was the first in the vicinity.

*   *   *

Early in 1920, through the generosity of a wealthy industrialist and the discreet researches of a committee of well-wishers, a handsome book was presented to every man of the town and district who had served in His Majesty's Forces; and to the next of kin of all those who had not returned home. Its cover was embossed with the flags of Britain and her Allies, and, in large gold letters, the title: 'Local Heroes of the Great War'. Its shiny pages (nearly 400 of them) were solemn with the faces (some three, some five, some 12 to a page) of the men who had died:

'Second-Lieutenant J. A. C. Spencer, 9th West Yorkshire Regiment, only son of Mr and Mrs J. W. Spencer, Lidget. Reported missing, August, 1915. Aged 24 years . . .'
'Sergeant Arthur D. Blackburn, Duke of Wellington's Regiment, Rushton Avenue, killed in action, August, 1918. Aged 18 years . . .'
'Private Charles H. Jones, Lancashire Fusiliers, Goschen Street, died of wounds, July, 1916. Aged 19 years . . .'

Not one of the faces smiled. Glumly they gazed at the camera (their photographs taken on furloughs, walking out stiffly in their uniforms), absurdly young beneath their caps and badges, throats buttoned tight into their coarse tunics. A sense of mortality lay sternly upon them.

'Seaman George Earnshaw, H.M.S. *Defence*, Church Street, killed in action, June, 1916. Aged 18 years . . .'
'Private Thomas Hurst, Durham Light Infantry, Tubber Hill, missing since 12th April, 1918; since officially presumed dead. Aged 20 years . . .'

Gradually, life was returning to what everybody hoped would be normal. Committees, suddenly unnecessary, had been disbanded. Lathes from the munitions factories had been auctioned off, mountains of ammunition boxes reduced to firewood. Ex-prisoners-of-war had been welcomed home, and all save the most grievous cases had limped, or been led, or wheeled, out of military hospitals.

Right *A Wiffan Waffan Wuffan Comic Band. Their elaborate 'instruments' are purely for appearance, being fitted to twopenny tin 'tommy-talkers' or 'voice disguisers'.*

('Rifleman Louis Sedgwick, King's Royal Rifles, Neville Street, officially reported killed, October, 1916. Aged 19 years . . .')

The great peace celebrations had come and gone, when streets and mills, inside and out, had blazed with flags. An enthusiastic albeit slightly self-conscious procession had mustered fancy-dress John Bulls and Britannias galore, tableaux with titles like 'The Dawn of a New World', and comic bands wearing German helmets and big red noses, blowing roisterously through tommy-talkers.

('Private Frank Smith, Duke of Wellington's Regiment, Castle Street, killed in action, November, 1918. Aged 21 years . . .')

Everywhere, subscriptions were being canvassed with a view to memorials. At the Mission, an ornate sycamore plaque had been unveiled, inscribed with 17 names, with a ledge underneath for flowers. The Parish Church were planning on a grander scale; there was talk of a stained-glass window and something in marble. In a far corner of his yard, an artistic monumental mason could occasionally be seen working on a statue for the cemetery, a rather unconvincing soldier in soft white stone, his helmeted head bowed and his webbing all wrong. The town as a whole dreamed of a Memorial Institute complete with a dance-floor, and a tennis-court round the back.

('Private Tom Langman, Duke of Wellington's Regiment, Broughton Road, died from gas poisoning, May, 1915. Aged 23 years . . .')

At any rate, land had been set aside for a Memorial Park whose centre would be a tall bronze winged Victory high on a pedestal surrounded by long bronze lists of the lost. A pleasant patch of sloping copse, its branches merry with bird-song and the Beck clattering at its foot, a start had been made on its careful rearrangement. Here and there, boulders had been dug up to make a rockery, and paths mapped out amongst the trees.

It was there, coming home from work one evening, that Arthur saw a small but vociferous crowd. They were shuffling about in churned level grass near the road, and out of the hubbub of their voices he caught phrases like 'ugly monster' and 'blooming wretch'. In their midst, just trundled up from the railway station, clean and polished and painted with green camouflage, stood a German field gun.

'We've seen enough of such things', one man, stamping his old Army boots, summed up the general mood. 'What do they want to remind us of those terrible times for?'

The German gun remained a subject of debate for days. A War Office Trophies Committee, it transpired, was despatching items of 'captured enemy stores' all over the country. A damaged machine-gun and several gigantic shell-casings had indeed occupied a glass case at the museum for some months, attracting no small interest. But the field gun, intended to cock its lean nose treewards, its wheels locked in cement, in perpetuity beside their future War Memorial, struck rawly at the town's emotions.

('Private Clifford G. Unwin, Duke of Wellington's Regiment, aged 23 years; Private James M. Varley, Duke of Wellington's Regiment, aged 30 years; Private Thomas S. Wigglesworth, Duke of Wellington's Regiment, aged 19 years ... Killed in action, July, 1916.')

The public gallery was nearly full, the night of the next Town Council meeting. Men and women, who had never before set foot in the panelled Council Chamber, gazed down awe-struck on the tops of Councillors' heads, the Town Clerk's long grey wig, and the red-robed Mayor sitting in state behind his great golden mace. Controversial item on the agenda was the German field gun.

'Suppose it is offensive to the bulk of the inhabitants', one Councillor queried, 'can we sell it for old iron?'

'We cannot sell it for old iron', the Town Clerk smoothly interposed, raising a laugh, 'it is largely steel'.

It soon became apparent which way the Councillors' discussion blew. This gun, it was emphasized, had no direct association with any of 'our lads'; it had never fired a shot in anger, having been captured

Right *The German field gun dumped in the Beck.*

78

unused. Many other towns had already accepted them. Such trophies had an educational value, and we should never allow our children to forget what the war had been like. ('Boy First-Class Frank R. Pollard, H.M.S. *Vanguard*, son of Mr and Mrs Frank Pollard, killed by the blowing up of his ship, July, 1917. Aged 17 years.') When two or three of the public tried to shout out, the Mayor threatened to clear the gallery. So the German field gun stayed.

And accounted, a few nights later, for Arthur's single, and wholly uncharacteristic, lapse into adult lawlessness: a half-planned, half-spontaneous gesture on the part of six or eight of his contemporaries aided by a few looking-for-mischief youngsters who should have been in their beds. They didn't even wait till it was properly dark, or bother about who might see them: just trampled into the top end of the Memorial Park and sent the German gun careering down the slope.

It was remarkably easy—one concerted heave and the gun was swishing away through the dusk-grey grass. Near the bottom, it

toppled over and hit the stony Beck with a mighty splashing reverberation that must have roused the entire town; followed by a tangible silence, in which one up-turned wheel remained slowly spinning. Men and boys scattered sheepishly to their homes.

Next day, people flocked to look; the day after, a photograph and story appeared in the papers; and the day after that, the police were seen to be making enquiries. Two called while Arthur was having his tea, a familiar elderly constable and new youngish sergeant. Arthur said he knew nothing about the gun, of course.

'I only wish', his mother forthrightly opined, 'that they'd taken the thing another half-mile and shoved it in the river'.

The constable started to talk sympathetically about only doing his job, but, at a hard look from the sergeant, trailed off in mid-sentence. Arthur promised to let them know if he heard anything about the culprits, and they left. That was the last he (or any of the others) ever heard of the matter.

Several evenings later, the German field gun made a thrilling return to its rightful position, watched by a sizeable crowd. A boisterous squad of former artillery drivers wrestled it upright, harnessed two horses and galloped it back up the slope to an accompaniment of cheers. Within hours, it was set solidly into a cement base. Eventually, the Memorial Park took mature shape around it, and winged Victory raised her metal laurels above it and her bronze catalogues of names: 'Lance-Corporal J. Jackson, King's Own Lancashire Regiment, killed in action, July, 1916. Aged 20 years . . . Second-Lieutenant G. W. A. Watson, Royal Air Force, killed in action, March, 1918. Aged 20 years . . .'

As the years went by, as children scrambled among the frozen spokes of its wheels and young men perched their giggling sweethearts on its high driver's seat, most people took their German gun for granted. When, during a later war, it was sent away for scrap, few even noticed that it had gone.

Right The work's 'Peace Trip', given by the mill-owners, for workers, 1919.

CHAPTER EIGHT

DEPRESSION

William Henry's return to the normal world was by no means easy. 'I say the "conchies" should remain in prison, or wherever they are, until all our boys come back into civil life', an anonymous letter-writer to the local paper voiced a popular opinion. 'I am proud to be a mother of three brave soldier sons, one having given his life for his country. I wonder what the "conchies" and their friends will feel like when they are asked what they did for freedom.'

Notwithstanding, William Henry emerged from custody in the spring of 1919. He was destitute, legally debarred from voting at elections for the next five years, had lost nearly three stones in weight, and was troubled by a persistent cough. There were dark circles round his eyes. He had to lie down and rest fairly often, and his hands tended to tremble. He began a weary round of applying for jobs, but with a prison record this was not easy. For several years he drifted from one temporary office desk to another. It was 1924 before he was able to teach again, and then he had to move away from home, into the Midlands.

But for Arthur, to begin with, 1920 seemed not greatly dissimilar from 1914. Old Eli had long since passed away, and his sons were rarely seen about the place, but Providence Mills functioned as usual and had, indeed, done rather well out of the war. They even celebrated a return to normal by treating their entire workforce to a day-trip to Windermere, hiring a convoy of charabancs for the journey and

cramming everybody aboard boats for a sail. Food was back in the shops again, and if prices had risen, so had wages. Even deadly anthrax was in the process of being conquered: potentially dangerous foreign wools would soon have to pass through a Government Disinfecting Station under construction at Liverpool.

Arthur rarely attended the Mission now, but only through a slow decline in interest—a loss of the habit—rather than any dramatic lack of faith. His left leg dragged a little, and his left shoes wore out more quickly than his right. He made a point of always taking them to a boot and clog repairer whose card read 'James Hey. (Late 1/6th West Riding Regiment). Trained at St Dunstan's, the Blinded Soldiers' and Sailors' Hostel. All Work Carefully Executed. Your Kind Orders are Solicited.'

In common with hundreds of thousands of his contemporaries, Arthur had been awarded the War and Victory Medals. The latter bore an inscription: 'The Great War for Civilization', but many ex-servicemen seemed to be enjoying few of the benefits of the victory or the civilization for which they had fought. Disabled trios and quartets in bits of uniform played ramshackle music wherever crowds gathered; pavement artists sat huddled in their old khaki greatcoats; in the streets you trod around the insides of caps, like big dirty mushrooms, cadging coppers.

Sometimes, outside the Post Office, a fine smart man would take up his stance, resplendent in his best Regular Army tunic of crimson, a Colour-Sergeant's burnished stripes on his sleeve and a row of Sudan, South African and Great War medals glittering across his chest. His blue eyes looked steadily before him; on his handsome face bristled a trim grey moustache pointed at either end; his proud back stood straight as a ramrod. And he came to a full stop just below the waist, with a square board on little wheels where his legs should have been—he could propel himself along by means of rubber pads in each hand. He never relaxed his expression of stern dignity. By his side leaned a notice: 'I Am Not Begging.'

The old Victorian workhouse was busier than ever before, thanks to the casual poor of no fixed abode. Every evening, alongside its tall railings, a row of ragged men waited for the gates to open and a bed for the night. All their worldly goods they humped around from town to town in bundles, bags and boxes. Every morning, before leaving, they each had to do a small job, and were then issued with a voucher for bread and cheese which they could claim at one of three shops strategically sited at the extreme edges of the town; for they were not encouraged to stay a further night.

When comfortably into his thirties, Arthur courted a young woman he had vaguely known as a girl in his boyhood years at the

Right *The girl hand-rolling cigarettes was on view* $5\frac{1}{2}$ *days at the Practical Tobacco Manufacturer's.*

Mission. Ethel Robinson was into her thirties too (she had lost a fiancé killed in the war), and made cigarettes by hand. Five and a half days a week, she sat with clean white blouse and deft fingers, on view in the shop-window of a Practical Tobacco Manufacturer, surrounded by slogans proclaiming to the world at large that Acme Gold Flake were Ten for Threepence and Guaranteed Free from Dust or Sand.

The courtship of Arthur and Ethel was not especially remarkable. In winter they went to dances (every chapel, club and public hall held dances) and did steady waltzes and fox-trots. When the tango came in, they never quite mastered it, and anyway Arthur's leg kept troubling him. On summer evenings they took sedate strolls along neighbouring lanes and up to the edge of the moors. Regularly twice every week—sometimes three times—they went to the pictures for a measured two hours of silent escapism: 'Do or Dare', 'Woman to Woman' ('plays on the emotions as do fingers on a harp'), 'The Rotters', 'Thundering Dawn' ('a picture that reaches the heights of human emotions! See the great typhoon and tidal wave that swept a whole city away! The most stupendous catastrophe shown in films!'). . . . Occasionally, they ventured on outings, bouncing up the Dales or into the Lake District on the solid tyres of open motor charabancs, cramped companionably six to a seat amongst their fellow-trippers and jocularly helping to unfurl the folding canvas hood when it rained.

After their marriage, they went to live in Clarendon Place, indistinguishable from Gladstone Street except that theirs, being an end house, was considered a cut above the rest. Ethel stopped making cigarettes in the tobacconist's window, and devoted herself to her husband and home. Providence Mills were not running quite so smoothly these days, and there were occasions when some departments didn't function at all; but, if wages dropped now and then, so to some extent did prices, and Arthur and Ethel got by.

When Ethel became pregnant, she did all the correct things. Women dying in childbirth were by no means rare, and in the poorer parts of town one baby out of six died in its first year. Periodically, the Medical Officer of Health inveighed against ignorance, against 'failure to breast-feed, failure to recognise the fact that the only possible substitute for mother's milk is its closest possible imitation, failure to keep baby's milk supply and bottle sterile, to protect baby against rapid changes of temperature, against dust-laden atmosphere caused by dry dusting and sweeping'.

For Ethel, however, there was no working at a factory till the last possible moment: she was free to attend a little clinic run by the Maternity and Child Welfare Committee and the Infant Aid Society in a few cavernous rooms of a former corn mill. She went to all their lectures for expectant mothers, and joined their sewing club. She learned about breast and artificial feeding, preparing baby-food, cot and clothing, weaning, clean milk, ventilation and cleanliness. She let the Home Visitor come and advise her, and, when her time arrived, had the midwife in (half the mothers of the town didn't). She gave birth to a baby girl called Mollie, which thrived for seven months then very nearly died, of measles.

*   *   *

In 1926, the miners came out on strike against pay reductions ('Not a penny off the pay, not a second on the day') and, as they were supported by railwaymen, dockers, drivers, printers, builders and engineers, a General Strike ensued. For nine days the normal patterns of life—trains, transport, supply, newspapers—moved only by fits and starts, or stopped altogether.

Arthur followed the news through the few daily duplicated sheets of a *Yorkshire Observer* which, besides outlining events, found room for sport, wool sales, weddings, theatre programmes, and occasional comment: 'This is no time for voluminous writing. It is the moment for action. At all costs the Government must be supported. Even any well-disposed people who do not like the Government must now support it. The alternative is anarchy. If the British people were to bow before anarchy all civilisation would be shaken to its foundations.'

Right *A charabanc outing—with caps on back-to-front!*

Anarchy, from the news as relayed by the *Observer*, seemed indeed to threaten. Non-striking tramcars pelted with lumps of coal in Leeds, windows of motor buses smashed, police baton charges through familiar streets. Strikers holding up a train at a level crossing at York. Heavy lorries chained to the rails at Middlesbrough in an attempt to wreck a passenger train. Four men carrying through Sheffield a machine-gun wrapped in brown paper. Nearer home, a milk train stoned—or so, at least, the headline had it: MILK TRAIN STONED. The reality was less flamboyant, the sole culprit a striking and confused plate-layer. 'I had had something to drink. The stones on the wall were loose', he told the magistrates unhappily. 'I only hit the engine once.' A crowd of people cheering him on shrank, on investigation, to a distinterested man and woman. The plate-layer got a month's hard labour.

At any rate, the Corporation trams were not running. Their younger drivers and conductors (Arthur's father, unwillingly on strike for the first time in his life, worried and fretted and stayed out of sight) went about in groups booing the private motor buses and charabancs which coolly took over their routes. Motorists displayed cards saying 'Signal for a lift', whilst some workers rode gaily to their factories in the backs of motor waggons. The *Observer* proffered advice to those on foot: 'The wise pedestrian now walks on the right-hand side of the road. Then he has a clear view of oncoming cars and is safely distant from overtaking traffic.' Volunteers rushed forward to enroll as engine-drivers and porters and special constables—so many, indeed, that most were never called upon.

It was dwindling coal supplies which proved the greatest problem and forced the worsted mills into a three-day week. And yet 'the

managers of the places of amusement', a local official kept his finger on the town's pulse, 'report that the strike has not made any difference in the numbers of their audiences'. The picture houses were variously showing 'Durand of the Bad Lands', 'Love and Sacrifice' and 'The Teaser', whilst the Hippodrome ran a light-hearted revue called 'What Ho!'

When the General Strike collapsed, with whatever repercussions in politics and the trade unions, Arthur saw Union Jacks flutter up flagpoles and sensed a public relief—'delight' was the word used by the resurrected newspapers. 'Crowds have congregated during the evenings in the centre of the town', the Emergency Food Officer turned in his final, retrospective report, 'but they have been crowds of good-natured, well-dressed people and anyone, not knowing that there was a serious crisis in existence, would have thought that a Gala Day was in progress. 'This', he concluded, 'is characteristic of the average British person'.

Only a handful of the more adamant tram-drivers and conductors found that they had maneouvred themselves out of jobs.

Unemployment in fact became the hallmark of the following years. The confusions of the post-war world, with traditional markets upset and foreign competition on the increase, were reflected even in the solid premises of Messrs Eli Wadsworth and Sons, still run along sound Victorian lines. From time to time it occurred to Arthur that he was overlooking some of the same machines he had known 30 years ago as a boy; that they now had less, not more, than 1000 workers employed; that the smooth processes stuttered with growing frequency, occasionally halting altogether. There was also the vexed question of wage reductions.

When the Wool Textile Employers' Council announced that all wages were to be cut by 11.7 per cent, the Association of Power Loom Overlookers protested 'most strongly' and pledged itself 'to use every endeavour to resist such action'. In reality, little was to be done. The National Union of Textile Workers ballotted its members with a view to striking, but a majority didn't even bother to vote. Some woolsorters did come out for a few days, but that, with hundreds looking for work, was a risky gesture, and they soon trickled back. Providence Mills became tinged with a new sense of bitterness.

Presently, work stopped altogether. After 80 years, Messrs Eli Wadsworth and Sons finished overnight with one word—liquidation. Most of their spinners and weavers couldn't understand the term, yet its results were final. At one stroke, liquidation killed Providence Mills stone-dead. The great sheds stood empty, looms and spindles silent. Liquidation locked the main gates, stifled smoke from the chimneys. Liquidation even called in surviving band instruments. Dust gathered alike on frames, skeps, bobbins, enamel mugs

Right *In these four beds slept a father, mother and seven children.*

forgotten, and old Eli's chair and table, long ago thrown down broken in a corner. Only a faithful old arthritic caretaker plodded pointlessly up and down and to and fro and round and round. . . .

So Arthur joined the multitudes on the dole: who scrimped and did without, went through their little savings, took their best suits and modest heirlooms to the pawnshops, slipped into debt, fell behind with the rent; who tramped round seeking odd jobs, chopped firewood, put notices in the corner shop, 'Man willing to work for next to nothing'; who scratched the tips in search of bits of coal and coke or cinders that still might burn; on whose, and whose children's behalf the Mayoress started a Clog Fund that raised money by community sing-songs ('Till we have built Jeroo-oo-oosalem'), and the Mayor, a League of Help distributing clothes, boots, food tickets, convalescent holidays and help with impatient landlords.

For a while, growing desperate and with time heavy on his hands, Arthur played in the Wiffan Waffan Wuffan Comic Band made up of unemployed ex-servicemen picking up coppers by busking round the public houses. They wore the craziest costumes they could devise, and their music, apart from a few drums and concertinas, emerged from tommy-talkers ingeniously connected to the spouts of old kettles and teapots. They would march miles to carnivals in neighbouring towns, doing knockabout sketches about parsons and policemen and women in prams. Main items in their repertoire were 'Sing As We Go' and 'Blaze Away!'

In 1931 the Government cut the dole by ten per cent and instituted the Means Test in an attempt to vary individual relief according to need. So an inspector from the Public Assistance Committee came to see Arthur, at a time when he and Ethel were boiling bones to make

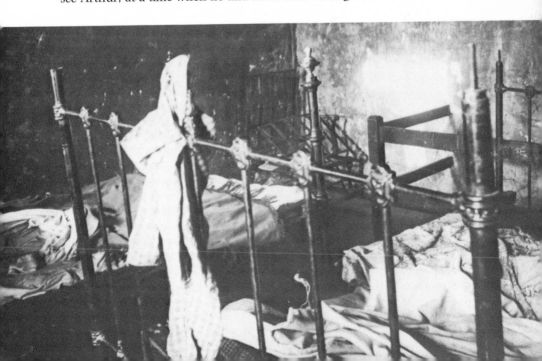

soup; their little girl's staple diet consisted of fish and chips and bread and margarine.

The Means Test inspector made a most thorough survey of the end house in Clarendon Place. He wanted to see Ethel's Savings Bank book (every last penny withdrawn, months ago), and Arthur's sick club card. He examined little Mollie's scooter, and asked how long she'd had it and who had bought it for her. He stared at the meal he had interrupted (this inspector, being exceptionally zealous, tried to make a point of calling at dinner-time whenever possible, so that he could check on what people were eating). He went into the front room and cast an experienced eye over the furniture. In the passage, he counted their coats. Upstairs, he checked the beds (just to make sure they hadn't one for a lodger), and poked into the bedding-box. Were any relatives, he wanted to know, helping them out financially or otherwise? (That was some hope, Arthur's father was far from well and kept being off work, whilst Ethel's mother was a struggling widow!) When it came to assessing how much the coppers busked with the Wiffan Waffan Wuffan Comic Band added up to (for Arthur's presence in their ranks had been duly noted by authority), Arthur flatly declared that he was renouncing the tommy-talker forthwith!

The Means Test roused a vocal minority of the unemployed to revolutionary fervour—'Down with the Means Test!' they cried, and 'Workers Rally Against Starvation!'—but it seemed there was little to be done. Some well-meaning townsfolk formed a Voluntary Migration Committee with the object of 'stimulating interest in overseas settlement'. One depressed loafer, who had been at school with Arthur and won a Military Medal during the war, threw himself in front of a train because he thought he was a burden to his friends. 'It is a great pity', observed the coroner, recording a verdict of suicide while of unsound mind, 'that a young man like that did not go abroad and try to better himself'.

In the autumn of 1932, Arthur joined a national hunger march— contingents from all points of Scotland and the industrial North tramping down to London to present a petition against the Means Test. The venture was not undertaken lightly: there were arrange- ments to be made, funds to be raised, footwear to be repaired. Down the rainy main roads marched shabby columns of men in raincoats and cloth caps, some with rolled blankets over their shoulders, some playing mouth-organs. It took weeks. On the way, they were given money, were lodged overnight in halls and Labour rooms, were fed by sympathetic committees. Arthur's leg gave out at Sheffield, so he missed the London culmination—the massive meeting (100,000 present, it was said) in Hyde Park, stones thrown, sticks wielded, mounted and foot police charging with batons near the Marble Arch, arrests, rain falling at night on lost marchers huddling in shop-doors

Right *The unemployed issue their own newspaper*: Means Test and Wage Cut Special.

and entrances to the Tube stations, dispersing to spartan billets in the suburbs. Their petition (claimed to comprise a million signatures) was never delivered.

So it was back home to the Temperance Society club-rooms opened, during the long grey winter days, for the unemployed to play draughts and chess in. There was even some equipment for men who might wish to do a little cobbling—strictly out of personal interest, of course, not for trade. Some of the more enterprizing were taught to make mats. It was possible to make quite passable mats out of bits of old rope.

Alternatively, there was the public library reading-room, where men could sit in the warm so long as they had a magazine in front of them (the janitor had orders to watch out for anybody loitering or nodding off, which was against the bye-laws). The thumbed newspapers made grim browsing, like the story of the local father of three prosecuted in November for not divulging that he had been haymaking on 22 June and thereby drawing $4s$ $6\frac{1}{2}d$ dole to which he was not entitled. 'If it had not been for your little children', the magistrates lectured him, fining him £1 and costs, 'you would have been far more severely dealt with. I am not sure that you would have been let off with a fine'.

At last, after nearly two years, Arthur got another job, in a new factory, manufacturing ladies' stockings. According to the advertising, he was helping to 'supply the demands of fashion', and was even 'creating fashion with beautiful designs', but that was a minor consideration to Arthur. The same factory made men's body belts and jockstraps. There was a lot of machinery, and Arthur was good with machines. Before very long—as he had done so many years ago with Messrs Eli Wadsworth and Sons—he was being promoted.

Below *From the* Means Test and Wage Cut Special.

FOUR SHILLINGS A WEEK

ONE or four shillings is what working women are going home with from the Labour Exchange in Todmorden at the end of the week.

After working one week, those who sign on every other week, are allowed 10s. per week under the Means Test, with a deduction of 3s. for every day worked. Thursday, Friday and Saturday of the week worked are counted as three days worked in the Exchange week, with the result that 9s. is deducted, leaving the women on short time 1s. to draw. On starting work on the Monday of the following week they have another 9s. deducted for Monday, Tuesday and Wednesday, result, 1s. to draw again.

If Saturday morning is payed, then Thursday and Friday are counted as worked, deduction 6s. and 4s. left to draw. On some occasions women have come out with as little as fourpence.

D. N.

MINORITY MOVEMENT HELPS UNEMPLOYED

(Continued from page 6.)

on a big scale were defeated, due to the work of the Building Trades M.M. These proposals would have

CHAPTER NINE

HOMES FIT FOR HEROES

During the 1920s, and continuing through the 1930s, the town changed physically. A new suburbia of highly desirable residences ('Your Home Is Your Castle!' cried the glossy brochures) crept steadily outwards, gobbling up fields, farms, barns, walls, stiles, water-troughs, lanes, footpaths, even the fringes of moorland hitherto unbroken. Tumbling streams were diverted, confined within pipes and channels or pushed under culverts; pools were drained, trees lopped. Builders vied one with another in the extolling of their 'sunny, restful estates' and their 'ideal positions'. On the brighter side of town, a south-facing hillside sprouted detached and semi-detached houses and a new incongruous name—Happy Valley. ('If you have a large enough deposit at the Bank or Building Society', the brochures advised, 'then all you need to do is consult your Architect or Builder, and choose a site'.)

At Happy Valley the gardens (as advertised) overflowed with apples, pears, plums and raspberries. When, on winter afternoons, the middle of the town lay in shadow, the sun still shone on Happy Valley. From proud frontroom windows the views were magnificent, even at night when householders could feast their eyes upon 'a panorama of lights, especially before factory closing time'. For the benefit of residents with motor cars, particular attention was being lavished on the provision of good roads and space for garages. ('If you don't keep a balance at the Bank, but have money lent to business concerns', persisted the brochures, 'then by depositing sufficient shares or other Scrip of value your Banker will no doubt give you the necessary credit.') One imaginative builder, harking back to the war, had coined a phrase: 'Homes Fit For Heroes to Live In!'

There were, of course, many heroes in the town itself who possessed neither the wherewithal nor indeed, in some cases, the incentive to move out to the delights of Happy Valley and similar suburbs; for whom the Council commenced an idealistic rehousing programme, covering further fields and farms with a tidy pattern of square pebble-dashed homes. Council houses stood 12 to an acre (in parts of the old town the average had been 66 to the acre), each with a garden of hard earth mixed with rubble, which tenants were hopefully expected to cultivate. What was perhaps even more to the purpose, every home had three bedrooms, a scullery, and its own bath and toilet.

So, as the new houses became available, slum-dwellers and their meagre possessions moved out of squalid alleys. Families of five, six, seven or more, who had slept in one bedroom, who had inhabited cellar-dwellings, rooms off iron balconies, hovels riddled

91

with tuberculosis and rickets. Mothers accustomed to finding bugs in the beds and their food nibbled by rats. Children who had grown up playing on dismal doorsteps, using outside lavatories, filling buckets at outside taps, and who had never had a proper bath with hot water. The first Corporation tenants, on raw hillsides where the breezes blew cool and wet but undoubtedly fresh, happily made tea for the builders' men, walked planks over unfinished roads and (to begin with, till the novelty waned), filled with unexpected pioneer enthusiasms, built rockeries, laid crazy paving and planted bulbs on their new garden plots.

Then, at last, the worst parts of town were demolished, starting (just 47 years after a Medical Officer of Health had first condemned it!) with the Ginnel. Down came the Rileys' old home—though the Rileys had long since moved on and out of local ken, as had the now middle-aged woman with a grown-up daughter who might have been young Harry's. Down came fractured walls, bulging gable-ends, sagging roofs, broken chimney-pots, cracked tiles, decayed plaster, dampness and smells and woodworm, reduced to heaps of unsavoury ruin beside the poisoned lower reaches of the litter-choked Beck. Down, too, came the occasional Elizabethan remnant or soiled Georgian frontage, the deteriorated coaching-inn, fragments of folk-history.

Down came the old slaughter-house tucked away behind the Ginnel, reeking of excrement and fearful with noises. For as long as anybody could remember, cows and sheep and pigs had been driven thither along the narrow alleys where, sensing death, they had sometimes run astray and been chased after through half the town. Boys had begged bladders to blow up as footballs, had climbed the slaughter-house wall and watched killing in the yard. Just once Arthur had tried: he had seen a man, pulling a chain through an iron ring, drag a cow's head to the ground; a second pair of brawny arms had raised aloft a pole-axe, to smash it down into the beast's forehead—provided the man with the chain could hold the cow's head steady, he had a reasonable chance of striking true; but Arthur, scrabbling backwards off the wall, had not waited for the outcome.

The old slaughter-house was replaced by a Municipal Abattoir outside the town. On the Saturday of its official opening, the public were invited in for conducted tours, and Arthur went along. Explanatory leaflet in hand, he walked around echoing vistas of fresh new buildings, clean-smelling and as yet unused: Lairage Pens, Beast and Sheep Slaughter Hall, Pig Killing Hall, Cooling Hall, Dressing Hall, Bleeding Passage, Tripery, Salt and Barrel Stores, Offal and Fat Stores, Gut Store, Hide Store. . . . After a while, the very precision of the place overwhelmed him ('The pigs are stunned in ingeniously-contrived pig traps, which are an innovation. The pig to be slaughtered is run down a passage, and at the end is caught between two sloping boards and immediately stunned. Then the trap turns over and the pig is lifted by a quick-acting hoist over a bleeding tray . . .') and he came away.

Eventually, nothing remained in the old heart of town except the Corn Mill Chimney, 80 feet tall and left till the last by which time it had plenty of open space to fall into. For decades, the Corn Mill Chimney had been rumoured unsafe, yet its destruction proved more difficult than anybody had anticipated. For two whole days, workmen hacked away at its base with chisels and sledge-hammers; and for two days everybody passing to work snatched a minute to watch, rushed out at dinner-time, dallied again on the way home, and waited again during the long summer evenings. By the second evening, 3,000 (held back at a respectable distance) were watching. The Corn Mill Chimney had loomed above Arthur's entire life, and when at last it fell, exactly along the line the steeplejacks had intended, it was gone in a matter of seconds. From every one of the 3,000 open mouths came an involuntary 'ooh' or 'aah' and, as the huge cloud of dust and soot settled, there suddenly seemed an undue amount of sky!

On the site there arose, very soon afterwards, a new red-brick Maternity and Child Welfare Clinic. Most of its windows were large and caught any available sun, and the walls of its waiting and weighing rooms, its dispensary, and the office where they distributed advice, milk and orange juice, shone cheerfully in pastel shades of pink and blue.

Arthur and Ethel had reason to be thankful for such changes. In the first place, Ethel (despite complications, and of course she wasn't getting any younger) had another baby, a little boy called Brian who thrived and grew plump; and in the second, they moved into one of the new Council houses.

Clarendon Place—and, for that matter, Peel Place and Gladstone Street—had for some years been following a process colloquially known as 'going down'. The expanding town had tended to draw its

more enterprising citizens outwards into the newer suburbs (Mr Berridge had done exceptionally well with the Co-operative Society, and had long ago moved away to Manchester), leaving the grey Victorian streets to the elderly and the less energetic. Most of the little square gardens lay neglected, and the lace curtains at many of the windows had a seldom-washed appearance. Very few housewives in Peel Place bothered now to whiten the edges of their doorsteps, as Mrs Illingworth did. Indeed, Arthur's father had died suddenly, just before he was due to retire; and, the same year that Arthur and Ethel moved into their Council house, his mother was lucky to find a home in the Charles Edward Rushworth's Almshouses.

Charles Edward Rushworth, last in the line of a substantial mill-owning family, had died during the war, but the finer points of his will had only recently come into effect, following the death of his widow. It had been his wish 'to provide a home for deserving aged or infirm persons who might otherwise be compelled to end their days in the Union Workhouse'; to which end, on the hilly outskirts of the town, behind a pleasant slope of lawn and shrubs and a high entrance bearing the words 'Charles Edward Rushworth's Almshouses', now stood a block of seven two-room dwellings in mock-Tudor style. In each living-room was a curtained alcove for a bed; from each kitchen led a little larder and a coal-place; and hot water went into each home by way of push-down taps ('When the pressure of the hand is released', for this was a novel feature that needed explanation, 'the supply stops'). There was a communal wash-house at one end of the block, and a bathroom at the other.

Mrs Illingworth was neither infirm nor particularly aged, but qualified as the tenant best able—in the phraseology of the late Charles Edward Rushworth, who had thought of everything—to 'perform the necessary light work appertaining to the exterior tidiness and cleanliness of the Almshouses'. She was allowed to take her own furniture, with which she packed her living-room and kitchen; and what she hadn't space for, she passed on to Arthur and Ethel. It was perhaps fortunate that Mrs Illingworth had always voted safely Liberal, since Charles Edward Rushworth had decreed, most emphatically, that inmates should not be 'members or supporters of what are commonly known as the Socialist Party and the Labour Party'!

*   *   *

For Arthur and Ethel now began a life of comparative comfort. Everywhere, on advertising hoardings and from newspaper and magazine pages, poured forth the blandishments of possession. It was easy (to begin with) to furnish a house. 'Big Bargains on the Easiest

Right *A display in a typical grocer's shop of this period.*

Terms!' trumpeted the big shops. 'Meet your Friends at the Civil Service Furnishing Depot and Spend a Pleasant Hour!' You didn't even need money, you could take advantage of a range of Deferred Payment Departments, weekly or quarterly arrangements.

Two shillings per week made you the proud owner of a 'three-piece suite, upholstered in hide-effect with loose Venetian cushions, along with a dainty china cabinet'. For half-a-crown weekly you could have the complete living-room, 'consisting of oak sideboard, pull-out extending dining table, two dining chairs, delightful three-piece suite in striped tapestry, and lino square'. Another half-crown bought the 'figured oak bedroom suite with full-length wardrobe; triple-mirror dressing table with two drawers; useful chest and full-size bedstead; lino square, rug, curb, and bedroom mirror'. Similar arrangements applied to additional commodities like pianos ('A Piano in the Home is an Indication of Taste and Refinement').

Then, of course, there was the wireless. A Radio Relay Service was supplying 5,200 hours of news and entertainment a year ('Order Today—Listen Tomorrow'), so 'we invite you to let us give you a demonstration at your home without obligation'. Of course, once

The Natural
Healer
for all
Skin Troubles

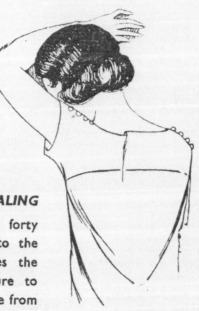

SOOTHING : CLEANSING : HEALING

Flesh-coloured Dressing with over forty years' reputation. It sinks deep into the pores of the skin, quickly eliminates the destructive elements and assists nature to build up new skin of perfect texture free from all blemish. The first application is wonderfully soothing, and the worst cases quickly yield to its healing power.

Don't be distressed,
Kurem Clears

you'd heard snatches of the BBC Dance Orchestra directed by Henry Hall, and the Kentucky Minstrels, and the Wireless Military Band, and Joan and Betty's Bible Story for the Children, and bits of a Francis Laidler Pantomime . . . why, you couldn't be expected to resist paying your weekly shilling or so and tuning in!

Clothes had discovered uses other than the utilitarian: 'Ladies— Our cut gives that SLIMMING EFFECT, and our styles will please your INDIVIDUAL PERSONALITY! Gents—Plus Fours, with caps to match, from the NEW BRILLIANT TWEEDS!' Multiple tailors could make a new man of you for 50 shillings and positively no extras. 'Seems I must have jumped in at the right moment, just when the stuff was hot from the mills', the square-jawed, pipe-smoking gentleman in the advertise-ments was smugly saying. 'Hence this lordly suit—cut, fitted and ready a split month before the world gets to hear of it. My friends are gnashing their teeth with envy over my new Spring Suit.'

Springtime, naturally, was hat-time: 'Smart, inexpensive hats in all the newest colours . . . Made in the new, greatly-in-demand styles . . . Tiny turbans, and fez fashions in the new straws'. And under the hat, for ladies, permanent waving ('Any head, any hair, any wave you desire'), and cosmetics: 'Let us show YOU how to emphasise your natural charm by the discreet use of our Toilet Creams and Powders—Advice FREE OF CHARGE on the correct use of day and evening make-up!'

Not forgetting health and vitality. There was Phosferine for 'Re-Inforced Beautifying Energy' ('When playing a rather tiring comedy part', the Brilliant Young Stage and Film Star Miss Gillian Lind felt able to assure the public, 'there is such a tax on the nerves in endeavouring to gain just the right effects, and Phosferine is by far the best means of rallying one's flagging energies, and for rejuvenating sparkling vigour'); Allenburys Diet to 'attract blood to the digestive organs, relieve the brain and soothe the nerves'; a hot lemon drink and two 'Aspro' tablets to 'Smash Up a Cold or 'Flu Attack in One Night'; Gold Medal Mint Rock to 'warm, comfort, soothe, and assist breathing'; shredded wheat ('Made in England from Empire Wheat Only'); and Bourn-Vita for 'a glorious night's sleep'.

And increasingly, Special Bargains in Second-Hand Vehicles: 'Morris Cowley Saloon. Colour Maroon. In very nice condition', £60 . . . Vauxhall Saloon. Blue, £35 . . . 12 hp Fiat two-seater, £25 . . . Morris Oxford Coupé, £15. . . .

Ultimately, you found yourself working over-time in an attempt to sustain a style of living somewhat in excess of what you could comfortably afford!

CHAPTER TEN

THE EVENTFUL THIRTIES

In 1931 Japan invaded Manchuria, and there was a revolution in Spain. In 1932 Japan attacked China, the Nazis emerged as the largest single party in the German Reichstag, and Britain, France, Germany and Italy issued a No Force Declaration deprecating the use of arms in settling international differences. The British Union of Fascists was founded.

At home, the man in the street was obsessed with sport. The year the town's Rugby League Football Club won through to the Cup Final at Wembley, everybody went wild with excitement. 'Whatever the result of the game', the local press grandly predicted, 'history will have been made'. Shopkeepers in a body extended their best wishes, and the Chamber of Trade got up special window displays and slogans, selling unaccustomed quantities of Wembley ties, Wembley raincoats, Wembley socks, Wembley binoculars and tricolour button-holes. 'Shout at Wembley!' a greengrocer advertised. 'Bananas for Strength! Fruit for Health! Salads for Energy! Vegetables for Vitality!' whilst an enterprizing cobbler waxed into verse:

> *If to Wembley you would like to go,*
> *And can't afford the fares,*
> *Set off a week before, or so—*
> *On 'New Road Side' Repairs.*

The team became virtually the sole topic of male conversation, and for weeks the papers were full of their training programme. For the last few days the players were all sent to Morecambe for 'sea air and sunshine'. Photographs poured back into town showing them sprinting up slipways, playing leapfrog on the promenade, paddling even. 'The cup-men may eat all they want, within reason', the sports reporters wrote home. 'They may go to a theatre at night, and they may read, talk, play billiards for a while afterwards. But they haven't to be too long. They may walk on the promenade, run a little, skip a little.' Their staple diet consisted of fish and toast, and naturally 'wives sweethearts and friends have all been left behind'. Arriving in London two days before the match, they laid a wreath on the Cenotaph.

Then a successful businessman realised that, of the Northern thousands flocking to 'the thrills and excitement at the Empire Stadium', many would be visiting the Metropolis for the first time. 'It is more than likely', he foresaw, 'that they will be bewildered by the transport system there'; and proceeded to circularize a daunting leaflet of routes to Wembley: the LMS Railway from Euston, the LNE

from Marylebone, the Metropolitan from Baker Street . . . London
Transport trolley-buses (Route 662) from Paddington, Green
Line Coaches (Route B) and Red Bus Services (Routes 8 and 92), and
of course the Bakerloo Tube ('travellers can follow their progress by
means of the diagrams displayed in every carriage'). . . .

In the event, 10,000 townsmen left for London aboard 16 trains
(extra porters were drafted in to load up a thousand crates of bottled
beer), the majority of whom reached the Empire Stadium more or less
safely. Their team scored a goal and a try but lost by 13 points—'a
plucky and valiant attempt', as their President later expressed it, 'to
crown the Club's jubilee year with a really precious jewel'. The
disappointed players (reunited at last with their wives, sweethearts
and friends) were regaled with a banquet at the Café Royal and a
'tumultuous welcome' home, driving round the crowded streets in an
open bus preceded by two brass bands. They never got to Wembley
again.

In 1933 Adolf Hitler was appointed Chancellor of Germany and
formed a Nazi cabinet. A Reichstag fire was blamed on the
Communists, civil liberties and freedom of the press were suspended,
German trade unions suppressed, and the persecution of Jews in
Germany begun. In November elections, 92 per cent of the German
electorate voted for Nazi candidates. In Spain, the Fascist Party was
founded.

The great outdoors was beckoning. Cyclists span along the lanes in
shoals, carried their bicycles over mountains, rode for favourite farms

Right *The cult of the outdoors: camping and cycling.*

101

and cottages where they consumed large quantities of home-made bread and jam with mugs of strong tea. Vulnerable white legs of adventurous men and women appeared in shorts; they flocked into the fields and woods burdened with tents and portable stoves. The Youth Hostels Association made available cheap overnight accommodation, and the gentler sex shouldered their own rucksacks and hiked off coequal with the male. There were disputes over rights of way and access to the countryside; the interests of landowners, water authorities and grouse-shooters were challenged. Occasionally, ramblers organised mass trespasses on controversial moorlands, resulting in unseemly fracas with gamekeepers and policemen. But rapidly, white legs turned brown and hardened.

Sometimes Arthur felt nostalgic, recalling spring-like stirrings of his youth; then realised that he had become a responsible family man, no longer young, with a left leg always liable to let him down.

In 1934 Hitler became Führer, wielding sole executive power in Germany. Dollfuss, Chancellor of Austria, was murdered. A purge of the Russian Communist Party began. King Alexander of Yugoslavia was assassinated.

Holidays were longer now, with pay. Excursion trains and buses went nearly everywhere, but Arthur wasn't satisfied until he could buy his own car, a little third or fourth-hand Austin Seven with a sunshine-roof out of which Mollie and Brian loved to poke their heads. The motor car had brought adventure within reach of the lucky family, making accessible both highways and byways; even—for the more reckless driver—green lanes and stony tracks. Sometimes they got stuck, fell into ditches, ran out of petrol or water (on Bank Holidays the roadsides were punctuated with fathers of families mending tyres and crawling into or under the workings of their vehicles), but really this was all part of the excitement. Quite suddenly, the horse became a rarity. Town streets suffered a new congestion, noisy and smelly. Cobbled market squares filled with motor cars. Ubiquitous families motored to lakes and seasides, bounced over hump-backed bridges, were waved aboard ferry-boats, drove right on to docks and the ends of jetties, parked on foreshores and the fringes of village greens. People took to eating picnics, reading the papers, and watching cricket matches and sunsets without even leaving their seats.

In 1935 Italy invaded Abyssinia. The Nuremberg Laws deprived German Jews of citizen rights. In 1936 the Spanish Civil War broke out. Germany reoccupied the Rhineland. Austria and Germany introduced conscription, and Germany and Italy recognised Franco's Nationalist government in Spain. The Olympic Games were held in Berlin.

Every second or third year, a German widow would visit the

Right Motor-car picnics at Heysham, 1933.

102

prisoner-of-war memorial in the Cemetery, laying on her husband's grave a wreath of pine fronds from the Black Forest. But one tranquil evening in 1936 occurred a visitation of a more sensational nature, in the shape of the German Zeppelin 'Hindenburg'. The 'Hindenburg' was the biggest airship ever built. Hydrogen-filled, she boasted a capacity of more than seven million cubic feet. Her lavish passenger accommodation included a dance-floor. She was 804 feet long and was supposed to be flying from the United States to Frankfurt, but had altered course and suddenly, out of the blue, appeared over a familiar moorland horizon.

Thousands rushed out, leaving their chores, their gardening, their wireless sets, their unfinished teas and their children's suppers. Very slowly, gently humming, the 'Hindenburg' floated across the town, so low that she seemed 'nearly touching the tree-tops' and 'blotting out the sky'. Along her great silver side could be read her number—LZ-129—the Olympic Games symbol, and on her tail were swastikas. The faces of her passengers gazed intently down. Over the middle of the town, a small parcel, trailing fluttering red ribbons, fell to earth. This contained a bunch of carnations, a crucifix of silver and jet, and a note: 'To the finder of this letter. Please deposit these flowers and this cross on the grave of my dear brother, Lieutenant Franz Schmitt, Prisoner-of-War in your Cemetery. God bless you!'

Which request—following a police and customs check—was complied with so far as concerned the carnations, although barriers had to be erected to keep souvenir-hunters at bay. The crucifix occupied the grave only briefly, for the benefit of British Movietone News, before going into the safe-keeping of the Roman Catholic Church.

Hundreds of citizens, in the excitement of the occasion, had grabbed their box-cameras and taken snapshots of the 'Hindenburg' overhead. These, for the most part, were photographically disappointing but, when considered together, vaguely disturbing: they showed (as nobody had noticed at the time) that the 'Hindenburg' had flown over most of the town, lingering especially above factories, foundries and

engineering works, railway-lines and goods-yard, main roads. A story circulated to the effect that she had been taking aerial photographs.

In 1937 Japan invaded China. There was religious persecution in Germany. German bombers destroyed the Spanish Republican town of Guernica.

A hundred Basque refugee children were brought over by a Spanish Relief Committee and housed in the old War Hospital, which had been allowed to fall into disrepair. Local volunteers, given a scant couple of weeks to prepare, scrubbed and disinfected, mended roofs and gutters, hacked at shrubs and privet hedges running riot between the buildings. Lorry-loads of gifts accumulated, chairs and tables, beds and bedding, wardrobes, pots and pans, a mangle and a sewing-machine, toys. The children arrived complete with Spanish cook, teacher, interpreter, and several beautiful young Spanish women helpers. Their matron, on the other hand, was formidable, elderly and English. They were frightened of the flashes from newspapermen's cameras, and some carried what purported to be letters from their parents ('We are Red as the poppy, but we are Red because they have shed our blood, and our bodies are stained with the red blood which runs in our veins'), almost certainly propaganda.

Townspeople were asked to 'adopt' a Basque child and invite him to tea. At some of the factories, workers contributed twopence a week each and thereby collectively maintained a child or two. Soon the Basques were growing vegetables in the old War Hospital grounds. When a team of Basque boys played football against local shop assistants, they had no football boots ('any spare pairs of boots will be very much appreciated') but won easily.

In 1938 Germany annexed Austria and occupied the Sudetenland. At the Munich Conference, Britain, France, Germany and Italy guaranteed the remaining frontiers of Czechoslovakia.

A photograph of William Henry Berridge appeared in most of the newspapers. He had got himself into the heart of the action in Spain, in beleaguered Madrid; although the caption didn't make it clear whether he was actually fighting or whether he was a member of some sort of political mission. William Henry looked as thin and worried as ever, and he had grown a straggly pointed beard, prematurely grey. An attractive girl Communist, young enough to be his daughter, hung with affection on his comradely arm.

In 1939 Italy invaded Albania. Britain and France recognised Franco's government in Spain, and Madrid fell to the Nationalists. Britain introduced conscription. Germany occupied Czechoslovakia and invaded Poland.

Through every letter-box dropped an official booklet called 'The Protection of Your Home Against Air Raids'. The head of the house was advised to consider himself as 'the captain of the ship' and

Right The 'Hindenburg' blots out the sky.

104

institute 'life-boat drill' accordingly. There was an immediate rush to buy dark blinds, and skylights were painted over. A few of the more prudent or pessimistic erected in their gardens the Standard Galvanised Corrugated Steel Shelter, as recommended by the Home Office.

Arthur's stocking factory was notified of its statutory obligation to provide air raid shelters for its workers, and creating fashion with beautiful designs gave place to problems of lateral and overhead protection, stability, emergency exits and debris loading. Indeed, air raid shelters were appearing everywhere, rather obtrusively, in parks and in the middles of grassy traffic roundabouts: unaccustomed earthy mounds with raw red-brick entrances whence steps descended into dank concrete catacombs. Props and timbers were hammered home in basements, shoring up their ceilings against hypothetical weights of buildings collapsing above. Slum demolition stopped, rows of dwellings being reprieved and their cellars reinforced. Council workmen were set to filling sandbags, mountains of them. In obedience to the new National Service Act, 20-year-olds departed, more or less reluctantly, to the Militia.

The government issued gas-masks. These came in three sizes, small, medium and large, and the recently-trained air raid wardens had the task of fitting them to the populace, on weekday evenings at the Mission. It was years since Arthur and Ethel had been inside the Mission, and its main hall looked different now. At one end, trestle tables were stacked with small, medium and large cardboard boxes.

'This respirator', explained the instructions, 'consists essentially of:– (i) a container filled with material to filter or absorb gas; and (ii) a facepiece to cover the eyes, nose and mouth'.

The old stencilled 'In All Thy Ways Acknowledge Him' had long ago been painted over, and the portrait of wealthy Mr Brigg consigned to the boiler-room. Now there was a high wooden pulpit in place of the simple old reading-desk, with fine waist-high rails to enclose the

choir: all of which could be dismantled whenever necessary (for they held dances there on Saturday nights). On the ledge beneath the sycamore plaque, with its 17 names of Great War dead, a little posy of wild flowers stood in a former fish-paste jar.

'The facepiece', continued the instructions, 'is made of rubber sheet, with a large window of non-inflammable transparent material. The cylindrical container is securely attached to the facepiece by means of a strong rubber band. All the air breathed by the wearer passes through this container, which removes the poisonous gas'.

At the trestle tables, people were helped experimentally into their gas-masks. Arthur, at the smell of rubber and his exaggerated breathing, remembered. . . . Mollie and Brian laughed, shrieking at each other, muffled behind their steamy eye-shields. On a form to one side, under the sycamore plaque, an elderly lady sat and wept. Men, women and children, successfully fitted, walked out with their new small, medium or large cardboard boxes swinging from their hands or looped over their shoulders with string.

That same summer, just before the schools broke up for the long holidays, Brian brought home a photograph of his class. Arthur compared it with his own Standard 3. The photographer was still working to the old five-row formula, but now the teacher, a pretty young woman, had come smilingly down into the middle of the second row. Now all the children were accustomed to cameras, and beamed. The sun shone full into the warm schoolyard, and all their coloured shirts and frocks were open at the throat. Their faces, and their plump knees, were as clean as healthy children's knees and faces can reasonably be expected to be!

Below *'As clean as healthy children's knees and faces can reasonably be expected to be'.*

ACKNOWLEDGEMENTS

Reminiscence and illustration have been forthcoming from many individuals. Special thanks are due to the resources of Keighley Public Library, notably its Great War ephemera collected by William Anderton Brigg and Herbert Arthur France (the former a Mayor, the latter a newspaper reporter); to Dr. John Prentice, for access to the papers of the late Dr. William Scatterty, Lt.-Col., R.A.M.C., War Hospital Administrator, 1916–1919; to Mr. Clement Bartrim, who wrote the verses on Page 48 whilst serving with the Lincolnshire Regiment; to Mr. Herbert Whitaker, for quotations from his coded diary of 1916; and to Mr. Michael Stephenson of Mills and Boon, the guiding force throughout this whole project.

Ian Dewhirst.